TEACHER'S GUIDE

Connected Mathematics 2 ™

W9-CUA-718

Bits and Pieces III

Computing With Decimals and Percents

Glenda Lappan
James T. Fey
William M. Fitzgerald
Susan N. Friel
Elizabeth Difanis Phillips

PEARSON

Boston, Massachusetts · Glenview, Illinois · Shoreview, Minnesota · Upper Saddle River, New Jersey

Connected Mathematics™ was developed at Michigan State University with financial support from the Michigan State University Office of the Provost, Computing and Technology, and the College of Natural Science.

This material is based upon work supported by the National Science Foundation under Grant No. MDR 9150217 and Grant No. ESI 9986372. Opinions expressed are those of the authors and not necessarily those of the Foundation.

The Michigan State University authors and administration have agreed that all MSU royalties arising from this publication will be devoted to purposes supported by the Department of Mathematics and the MSU Mathematics Enrichment Fund.

13-digit ISBN 978-0-13-366186-6
10-digit ISBN 0-13-366186-5
2 3 4 5 6 7 8 9 10   11 10 09 08

Authors of Connected Mathematics

(from left to right) Glenda Lappan, Betty Phillips, Susan Friel, Bill Fitzgerald, Jim Fey

Glenda Lappan is a University Distinguished Professor in the Department of Mathematics at Michigan State University. Her research and development interests are in the connected areas of students' learning of mathematics and mathematics teachers' professional growth and change related to the development and enactment of K–12 curriculum materials.

James T. Fey is a Professor of Curriculum and Instruction and Mathematics at the University of Maryland. His consistent professional interest has been development and research focused on curriculum materials that engage middle and high school students in problem-based collaborative investigations of mathematical ideas and their applications.

William M. Fitzgerald (*Deceased*) was a Professor in the Department of Mathematics at Michigan State University. His early research was on the use of concrete materials in supporting student learning and led to the development of teaching materials for laboratory environments. Later he helped develop a teaching model to support student experimentation with mathematics.

Susan N. Friel is a Professor of Mathematics Education in the School of Education at the University of North Carolina at Chapel Hill. Her research interests focus on statistics education for middle-grade students and, more broadly, on teachers' professional development and growth in teaching mathematics K–8.

Elizabeth Difanis Phillips is a Senior Academic Specialist in the Mathematics Department of Michigan State University. She is interested in teaching and learning mathematics for both teachers and students. These interests have led to curriculum and professional development projects at the middle school and high school levels, as well as projects related to the teaching and learning of algebra across the grades.

CMP2 Development Staff

Teacher Collaborator in Residence
Yvonne Grant
Michigan State University

Administrative Assistant
Judith Martus Miller
Michigan State University

Production and Field Site Manager
Lisa Keller
Michigan State University

Technical and Editorial Support
Brin Keller, Peter Lappan, Jim Laser, Michael Masterson, Stacey Miceli

Assessment Team
June Bailey and **Debra Sobko** (Apollo Middle School, Rochester, New York), **George Bright** (University of North Carolina, Greensboro), **Gwen Ranzau Campbell** (Sunrise Park Middle School, White Bear Lake, Minnesota), **Holly DeRosia, Kathy Dole,** and **Teri Keusch** (Portland Middle School, Portland, Michigan), **Mary Beth Schmitt** (Traverse City East Junior High School, Traverse City, Michigan), **Genni Steele** (Central Middle School, White Bear Lake, Minnesota), **Jacqueline Stewart** (Okemos, Michigan), **Elizabeth Tye** (Magnolia Junior High School, Magnolia, Arkansas)

Development Assistants
At Lansing Community College *Undergraduate Assistant:* **James Brinegar**

At Michigan State University *Graduate Assistants:* **Dawn Berk, Emily Bouck, Bulent Buyukbozkirli, Kuo-Liang Chang, Christopher Danielson, Srinivasa Dharmavaram, Deb Johanning, Wesley Kretzschmar, Kelly Rivette, Sarah Sword, Tat Ming Sze, Marie Turini, Jeffrey Wanko;** *Undergraduate Assistants:* **Daniel Briggs, Jeffrey Chapin, Jade Corsé, Elisha Hardy, Alisha Harold, Elizabeth Keusch, Julia Letoutchaia, Karen Loeffler, Brian Oliver, Carl Oliver, Evonne Pedawi, Lauren Rebrovich**

At the University of Maryland *Graduate Assistants:* **Kim Harris Bethea, Kara Karch**

At the University of North Carolina (Chapel Hill) *Graduate Assistants:* **Mark Ellis, Trista Stearns;** *Undergraduate Assistant:* **Daniel Smith**

Advisory Board for CMP2

Thomas Banchoff
Professor of Mathematics
Brown University
Providence, Rhode Island

Anne Bartel
Mathematics Coordinator
Minneapolis Public Schools
Minneapolis, Minnesota

Hyman Bass
Professor of Mathematics
University of Michigan
Ann Arbor, Michigan

Joan Ferrini-Mundy
Associate Dean of the College of
Natural Science; Professor
Michigan State University
East Lansing, Michigan

James Hiebert
Professor
University of Delaware
Newark, Delaware

Susan Hudson Hull
Charles A. Dana Center
University of Texas
Austin, Texas

Michele Luke
Mathematics Curriculum
Coordinator
West Junior High
Minnetonka, Minnesota

Kay McClain
Assistant Professor of
Mathematics Education
Vanderbilt University
Nashville, Tennessee

Edward Silver
Professor; Chair of Educational
Studies
University of Michigan
Ann Arbor, Michigan

Judith Sowder
Professor Emerita
San Diego State University
San Diego, California

Lisa Usher
Mathematics Resource Teacher
California Academy of
Mathematics and Science
San Pedro, California

Field Test Sites for CMP2

During the development of the revised edition of *Connected Mathematics* (CMP2), more than 100 classroom teachers have field-tested materials at 49 school sites in 12 states and the District of Columbia. This classroom testing occurred over three academic years (2001 through 2004), allowing careful study of the effectiveness of each of the 24 units that comprise the program. A special thanks to the students and teachers at these pilot schools.

Arkansas
Magnolia Public Schools
Kittena Bell*, Judith Trowell*; *Central Elementary School:* Maxine Broom, Betty Eddy, Tiffany Fallin, Bonnie Flurry, Carolyn Monk, Elizabeth Tye; *Magnolia Junior High School:* Monique Bryan, Ginger Cook, David Graham, Shelby Lamkin

Colorado
Boulder Public Schools
Nevin Platt Middle School: Judith Koenig

St. Vrain Valley School District, Longmont
Westview Middle School: Colleen Beyer, Kitty Canupp, Ellie Decker*, Peggy McCarthy, Tanya deNobrega, Cindy Payne, Ericka Pilon, Andrew Roberts

District of Columbia
Capitol Hill Day School: Ann Lawrence

Georgia
University of Georgia, Athens
Brad Findell

Madison Public Schools
Morgan County Middle School: Renee Burgdorf, Lynn Harris, Nancy Kurtz, Carolyn Stewart

Maine
Falmouth Public Schools
Falmouth Middle School: Donna Erikson, Joyce Hebert, Paula Hodgkins, Rick Hogan, David Legere, Cynthia Martin, Barbara Stiles, Shawn Towle*

Michigan
Portland Public Schools
Portland Middle School: Mark Braun, Holly DeRosia, Kathy Dole*, Angie Foote, Teri Keusch, Tammi Wardwell

Traverse City Area Public Schools
Bertha Vos Elementary: Kristin Sak; *Central Grade School:* Michelle Clark; Jody Meyers; *Eastern Elementary:* Karrie Tufts; *Interlochen Elementary:* Mary McGee-Cullen; *Long Lake Elementary:* Julie Faulkner*, Charlie Maxbauer, Katherine Sleder; *Norris Elementary:* Hope Slanaker; *Oak Park Elementary:* Jessica Steed; *Traverse Heights Elementary:* Jennifer Wolfert; *Westwoods Elementary:* Nancy Conn; *Old Mission Peninsula School:* Deb Larimer; *Traverse City East Junior High:* Ivanka Berkshire, Ruthanne Kladder, Jan Palkowski, Jane Peterson, Mary Beth Schmitt; *Traverse City West Junior High:* Dan Fouch*, Ray Fouch

Sturgis Public Schools
Sturgis Middle School: Ellen Eisele

Minnesota
Burnsville School District 191
Hidden Valley Elementary: Stephanie Cin, Jane McDevitt

Hopkins School District 270
Alice Smith Elementary: Sandra Cowing, Kathleen Gustafson, Martha Mason, Scott Stillman; *Eisenhower Elementary:* Chad Bellig, Patrick Berger, Nancy Glades, Kye Johnson, Shane Wasserman, Victoria Wilson; *Gatewood Elementary:* Sarah Ham, Julie Kloos, Janine Pung, Larry Wade; *Glen Lake Elementary:* Jacqueline Cramer, Kathy Hering, Cecelia Morris, Robb Trenda; *Katherine Curren Elementary:* Diane Bancroft, Sue DeWit, John Wilson; *L. H. Tanglen Elementary:* Kevin Athmann, Lisa Becker, Mary LaBelle, Kathy Rezac, Roberta Severson; *Meadowbrook Elementary:* Jan Gauger, Hildy Shank, Jessica Zimmerman; *North Junior High:* Laurel Hahn, Kristin Lee, Jodi Markuson, Bruce Mestemacher, Laurel Miller, Bonnie Rinker, Jeannine Salzer, Sarah Shafer, Cam Stottler; *West Junior High:* Alicia Beebe, Kristie Earl, Nobu Fujii, Pam Georgetti, Susan Gilbert, Regina Nelson Johnson, Debra Lindstrom, Michele Luke*, Jon Sorensen

Minneapolis School District 1
Ann Sullivan K–8 School: Bronwyn Collins; Anne Bartel* (Curriculum and Instruction Office)

Wayzata School District 284
Central Middle School: Sarajane Myers, Dan Nielsen, Tanya Ravnholdt

White Bear Lake School District 624
Central Middle School: Amy Jorgenson, Michelle Reich, Brenda Sammon

New York
New York City Public Schools
IS 89: Yelena Aynbinder, Chi-Man Ng, Nina Rapaport, Joel Spengler, Phyllis Tam*, Brent Wyso; *Wagner Middle School:* Jason Appel, Intissar Fernandez, Yee Gee Get, Richard Goldstein, Irving Marcus, Sue Norton, Bernadita Owens, Jennifer Rehn*, Kevin Yuhas

---

* indicates a Field Test Site Coordinator

Ohio

Talawanda School District, Oxford
Talawanda Middle School: Teresa Abrams, Larry Brock, Heather Brosey, Julie Churchman, Monna Even, Karen Fitch, Bob George, Amanda Klee, Pat Meade, Sandy Montgomery, Barbara Sherman, Lauren Steidl

Miami University
Jeffrey Wanko*

Springfield Public Schools
Rockway School: Jim Mamer

Pennsylvania

Pittsburgh Public Schools
Kenneth Labuskes, Marianne O'Connor, Mary Lynn Raith*; *Arthur J. Rooney Middle School:* David Hairston, Stamatina Mousetis, Alfredo Zangaro; *Frick International Studies Academy:* Suzanne Berry, Janet Falkowski, Constance Finseth, Romika Hodge, Frank Machi; *Reizenstein Middle School:* Jeff Baldwin, James Brautigam, Lorena Burnett, Glen Cobbett, Michael Jordan, Margaret Lazur, Tamar McPherson, Melissa Munnell, Holly Neely, Ingrid Reed, Dennis Reft

Texas

Austin Independent School District
Bedichek Middle School: Lisa Brown, Jennifer Glasscock, Vicki Massey

El Paso Independent School District
Cordova Middle School: Armando Aguirre, Anneliesa Durkes, Sylvia Guzman, Pat Holguin*, William Holguin, Nancy Nava, Laura Orozco, Michelle Peña, Roberta Rosen, Patsy Smith, Jeremy Wolf

Plano Independent School District
Patt Henry, James Wohlgehagen*; *Frankford Middle School:* Mandy Baker, Cheryl Butsch, Amy Dudley, Betsy Eshelman, Janet Greene, Cort Haynes, Kathy Letchworth, Kay Marshall, Kelly McCants, Amy Reck, Judy Scott, Syndy Snyder, Lisa Wang; *Wilson Middle School:* Darcie Bane, Amanda Bedenko, Whitney Evans, Tonelli Hatley, Sarah (Becky) Higgs, Kelly Johnston, Rebecca McElligott, Kay Neuse, Cheri Slocum, Kelli Straight

Washington

Evergreen School District
Shahala Middle School: Nicole Abrahamsen, Terry Coon*, Carey Doyle, Sheryl Drechsler, George Gemma, Gina Helland, Amy Hilario, Darla Lidyard, Sean McCarthy, Tilly Meyer, Willow Nuewelt, Todd Parsons, Brian Pederson, Stan Posey, Shawn Scott, Craig Sjoberg, Lynette Sundstrom, Charles Switzer, Luke Youngblood

Wisconsin

Beaver Dam Unified School District
Beaver Dam Middle School: Jim Braemer, Jeanne Frick, Jessica Greatens, Barbara Link, Dennis McCormick, Karen Michels, Nancy Nichols*, Nancy Palm, Shelly Stelsel, Susan Wiggins

---

* indicates a Field Test Site Coordinator

Reviews of CMP to Guide Development of CMP2

Before writing for CMP2 began or field tests were conducted, the first edition of *Connected Mathematics* was submitted to the mathematics faculties of school districts from many parts of the country and to 80 individual reviewers for extensive comments.

School District Survey Reviews of CMP

Arizona
Madison School District #38 (Phoenix)

Arkansas
Cabot School District, Little Rock School District, Magnolia School District

California
Los Angeles Unified School District

Colorado
St. Vrain Valley School District (Longmont)

Florida
Leon County Schools (Tallahassee)

Illinois
School District #21 (Wheeling)

Indiana
Joseph L. Block Junior High (East Chicago)

Kentucky
Fayette County Public Schools (Lexington)

Maine
Selection of Schools

Massachusetts
Selection of Schools

Michigan
Sparta Area Schools

Minnesota
Hopkins School District

Texas
Austin Independent School District, The El Paso Collaborative for Academic Excellence, Plano Independent School District

Wisconsin
Platteville Middle School

Individual Reviewers of CMP

Arkansas
Deborah Cramer; Robby Frizzell *(Taylor)*; Lowell Lynde *(University of Arkansas, Monticello)*; Leigh Manzer *(Norfork)*; Lynne Roberts *(Emerson High School, Emerson)*; Tony Timms *(Cabot Public Schools)*; Judith Trowell *(Arkansas Department of Higher Education)*

California
José Alcantar *(Gilroy)*; Eugenie Belcher *(Gilroy)*; Marian Pasternack *(Lowman M. S. T. Center, North Hollywood)*; Susana Pezoa *(San Jose)*; Todd Rabusin *(Hollister)*; Margaret Siegfried *(Ocala Middle School, San Jose)*; Polly Underwood *(Ocala Middle School, San Jose)*

Colorado
Janeane Golliher *(St. Vrain Valley School District, Longmont)*; Judith Koenig *(Nevin Platt Middle School, Boulder)*

Florida
Paige Loggins *(Swift Creek Middle School, Tallahassee)*

Illinois
Jan Robinson *(School District #21, Wheeling)*

Indiana
Frances Jackson *(Joseph L. Block Junior High, East Chicago)*

Kentucky
Natalee Feese *(Fayette County Public Schools, Lexington)*

Maine
Betsy Berry *(Maine Math & Science Alliance, Augusta)*

Maryland
Joseph Gagnon *(University of Maryland, College Park)*; Paula Maccini *(University of Maryland, College Park)*

Massachusetts
George Cobb *(Mt. Holyoke College, South Hadley)*; Cliff Kanold *(University of Massachusetts, Amherst)*

Michigan
Mary Bouck *(Farwell Area Schools)*; Carol Dorer *(Slauson Middle School, Ann Arbor)*; Carrie Heaney *(Forsythe Middle School, Ann Arbor)*; Ellen Hopkins *(Clague Middle School, Ann Arbor)*; Teri Keusch *(Portland Middle School, Portland)*; Valerie Mills *(Oakland Schools, Waterford)*; Mary Beth Schmitt *(Traverse City East Junior High, Traverse City)*; Jack Smith *(Michigan State University, East Lansing)*; Rebecca Spencer *(Sparta Middle School, Sparta)*; Ann Marie Nicoll Turner *(Tappan Middle School, Ann Arbor)*; Scott Turner *(Scarlett Middle School, Ann Arbor)*

Minnesota
Margarita Alvarez *(Olson Middle School, Minneapolis)*; Jane Amundson *(Nicollet Junior High, Burnsville)*; Anne Bartel *(Minneapolis Public Schools)*; Gwen Ranzau Campbell *(Sunrise Park Middle School, White Bear Lake)*; Stephanie Cin *(Hidden Valley Elementary, Burnsville)*; Joan Garfield *(University of Minnesota, Minneapolis)*; Gretchen Hall *(Richfield Middle School, Richfield)*; Jennifer Larson *(Olson Middle School, Minneapolis)*; Michele Luke *(West Junior High, Minnetonka)*; Jeni Meyer *(Richfield Junior High, Richfield)*; Judy Pfingsten *(Inver Grove Heights Middle School, Inver Grove Heights)*; Sarah Shafer *(North Junior High, Minnetonka)*; Genni Steele *(Central Middle School, White Bear Lake)*; Victoria Wilson *(Eisenhower Elementary, Hopkins)*; Paul Zorn *(St. Olaf College, Northfield)*

New York
Debra Altenau-Bartolino *(Greenwich Village Middle School, New York)*; Doug Clements *(University of Buffalo)*; Francis Curcio *(New York University, New York)*; Christine Dorosh *(Clinton School for Writers, Brooklyn)*; Jennifer Rehn *(East Side Middle School, New York)*; Phyllis Tam *(IS 89 Lab School, New York)*;

Marie Turini *(Louis Armstrong Middle School, New York)*; Lucy West *(Community School District 2, New York)*; Monica Witt *(Simon Baruch Intermediate School 104, New York)*

Pennsylvania
Robert Aglietti *(Pittsburgh)*; Sharon Mihalich *(Freeport)*; Jennifer Plumb *(South Hills Middle School, Pittsburgh)*; Mary Lynn Raith *(Pittsburgh Public Schools)*

Texas
Michelle Bittick *(Austin Independent School District)*; Margaret Cregg *(Plano Independent School District)*; Sheila Cunningham *(Klein Independent School District)*; Judy Hill *(Austin Independent School District)*; Patricia Holguin *(El Paso Independent School District)*; Bonnie McNemar *(Arlington)*; Kay Neuse *(Plano Independent School District)*; Joyce Polanco *(Austin Independent School District)*; Marge Ramirez *(University of Texas at El Paso)*; Pat Rossman *(Baker Campus, Austin)*; Cindy Schimek *(Houston)*; Cynthia Schneider *(Charles A. Dana Center, University of Texas at Austin)*; Uri Treisman *(Charles A. Dana Center, University of Texas at Austin)*; Jacqueline Weilmuenster *(Grapevine-Colleyville Independent School District)*; LuAnn Weynand *(San Antonio)*; Carmen Whitman *(Austin Independent School District)*; James Wohlgehagen *(Plano Independent School District)*

Washington
Ramesh Gangolli *(University of Washington, Seattle)*

Wisconsin
Susan Lamon *(Marquette University, Hales Corner)*; Steve Reinhart *(retired, Chippewa Falls Middle School, Eau Claire)*

Table of Contents

Bits and Pieces III

The Student Edition pages for the Unit Opener follow page 14.

Unit Introduction

Bits and Pieces III
Computing With Decimals and Percents

Goals of the Unit

- Build on knowledge about operations with fractions and whole numbers

- Develop and use benchmarks and other strategies to estimate the answers to computations with decimals

- Develop meaning of and algorithms for operations with decimals

- Use the relationship between decimals and fractions to develop and understand why decimal algorithms work

- Use the place value interpretation of decimals to make sense of shortcut algorithms for operations

- Generalize number patterns to help make sense of decimal operations

- Choose between addition, subtraction, multiplication, or division as an appropriate operation to use to solve a problem

- Understand that decimals are often associated with measurements in real-world situations

- Solve problems using operations with decimals.

- Use understanding of operations and the meaning of percents to solve percent problems of the form $a\%$ of b equals c for any one of the variables a, b, or c

- Create and interpret circle graphs

Developing Students' Mathematical Habits

The overall goal of the *Connected Mathematics* (CMP) curriculum is to help students develop sound mathematical habits. Through their work in this and other number units, students should ask themselves questions about situations that involve decimals and percents:

- *What is the whole (unit) in this situation?*

- *How big are the numbers in this problem?*

- *About how large will the sum (difference, product, or quotient) be?*

- *How do these decimals compare to fractions that I know?*

- *Why are percents useful in this problem?*

Overview

Rational numbers and their various forms of representation and interpretation are the heart of the middle-grades experiences with number concepts. In earlier units, students have explored various meanings of and models for rational numbers in fraction form and in decimal form. They have developed efficient algorithms for addition, subtraction, multiplication, and division with fractions. These algorithms will be one basis on which understanding of operations with decimals will be built. Here the meaning of decimals as special fractions with denominators that are powers of 10 will be the focus and help make the connection.

In elementary school, the place value chart is often extended to include digits to the right of the decimal point. However, this knowledge is very fragile for most students in grade six. Using a place value interpretation alone places a great deal of faith in number patterns to help students make sense of operations, especially of multiplication and division. We have chosen instead to use both a fraction interpretation and a place value interpretation of decimals to support the development of algorithms.

This unit is designed to provide experiences in building algorithms for the four basic operations with decimals, as well as opportunities for students to consider when such operations are useful in solving problems. For example, what signals indicate to the student that division will help solve a problem? Building this kind of thinking and reasoning supports the development of skill with the algorithms. We build on students' familiarity with money as an entry point and use other familiar measurement situations where measures are given in decimals.

As the title also implies, this unit uses the students' knowledge of operations with decimals to return to percents and to further develop students' understanding and skill in solving percent problems. Particular attention is paid to solving the relationship *a% of b equals c*, when only two of the three values *a, b,* and *c* are given. In many texts, the three cases for the missing variable are taught as separate, unrelated problems. We want students to see that finding a percent of a number, finding what percent one number is of another number,

and finding the original number if you know a percent of the number are all versions of this basic relationship with different unknown variables. In the case of finding a percent of a number, the unknown is *c,* for example, 5% of 24 equals *c.* In finding what percent one number is of another, the unknown is *a,* for example, *a*% of 48 equals 6. And, in finding the original number if you know the percent of the number, the unknown is *b,* for example, 15% of *b* equals 27.

Before we look at the specific mathematical ideas developed and used in this unit, it is helpful to review the ideas developed in *Bits and Pieces I* and *II* as these are the underpinnings for this unit.

CMP and Fractions: Review of *Bits and Pieces I* and *II*

In CMP, we have developed a set of connected units that comprise the rational number strand for grade six. In *Bits and Pieces I,* the first unit on fractions, decimals, and percents, the investigations ask students to make sense of the meaning of fractions, decimals, and percents in different contexts. The unit emphasizes developing an understanding of basic interpretations, models, equivalence, and ordering of rational numbers. Students learn to move among equivalent forms of fractions and to move among fractions, decimals, and percents. They also build benchmarks for estimating locations of rational numbers on a number line and begin to estimate simple sums and differences. The models introduced and used in *Bits and Pieces I* (fraction strips, bars, number lines, and area models) are continued and built upon in *Bits and Pieces II.*

In *Bits and Pieces II,* students develop algorithms for fraction computations. As is the case with other aspects of CMP, students are confronted with situations that call for putting together, taking apart, duplicating, counting an array, sharing, grouping, partitioning, measuring, etc. As they confront such situations, they not only learn to "do" addition, subtraction, multiplication, and division of fractions, but they also learn the meaning of the operations and the kinds of situations that call for each. As students work individually, in groups, and as a whole class on problems, they learn ways of thinking about and operating with fractions and they practice the algorithms to develop skill in carrying them out.

We expect students to finish *Bits and Pieces II* knowing algorithms for computation that they understand and can use with facility.

Interpretations of Fractions

The major interpretations of fractions students encounter in *Bits and Pieces I* and *II* are:

1. fractions as parts of a whole
2. fractions as measures or quantities
3. fractions as indicated division

Interpretations such as fractions as operators ("stretchers" or "shrinkers") and fractions as rates, ratios, or parts of a proportion are foreshadowed here and continued in later grades. For a fuller discussion of these ideas, please see the Teacher Guides to *Bits and Pieces I* and *II*.

Models of Fractions

The models of rational numbers used throughout CMP were chosen because they connect directly to important interpretations of rational numbers. The fraction models used for developing both meaning and the operations on them are:

1. fraction-strip models
2. number-line models
3. grid-area models
4. partition models

For a fuller discussion of these models please see the Teacher Guides to *Bits and Pieces I* and *II*.

Summary of Investigations

Investigation 1
Decimals—More or Less!

Investigation 1 develops addition and subtraction of decimals. One problem focuses on estimation strategies, as do other problems in the unit. The initial questions CMP helps students to ask are, "About how great will the answer be? What makes sense?" These give students a way to know if their computations, done by hand or by calculator, are at least close to the correct answer or obviously wrong. In many situations an estimate is sufficient to "solve" the problem or make the needed decision.

Other problems in Investigation 1 focus on the place value interpretation of a number and what that means for adding or subtracting numbers.

Addition-subtraction fact families are used to help solve for missing addends or sums in situations written in symbolic form. Students write mathematical sentences using symbols to indicate the required computation(s). An underlying goal of all this work is learning both to write and to read mathematical language. Additionally, students learn the value of changing the representation of fractions and decimals that they need to add or subtract to a form with common denominators, so that the numerators can be added or subtracted. Students' previous work in locating and representing fractions on the number line is critical to the development of common denominators as a strategy for adding or subtracting. In the end, students articulate an algorithm for adding and subtracting.

Investigation 2
Decimal Times

This investigation focuses on developing an algorithm for multiplying decimals. Students use fractions to help make sense of multiplication of decimals. They look at products, find missing factors, and use estimation as a way to determine where the decimal has to be in a product of decimal numbers. Problem 2.4 lays the groundwork for the simple shortcut algorithm: Multiply the decimals as whole numbers and adjust the place of the decimal in the product.

Investigation 3
The Decimal Divide

Investigation 3 develops an algorithm for division of decimals. In developing the algorithm, students solve a set of contextualized problems that provide a common sense way to think about decimal division based on what they already know about whole-number and fraction division. Students use the fraction form of decimals to develop an algorithm for dividing decimals. The last two problems look at patterns in division and in terminating and repeating decimals.

Investigation 4

Using Percents

In all three problems of Investigation 4, students look at real situations in which one encounters percents. The typical situations of discounts, taxes, and tips help students think about taking a percent of a number. The discount and tax situations help students to consider the amount left when a reduction is made and the total when taxes are added.

Investigation 5

More About Percents

In this investigation, students are asked to devise a general strategy for finding a percent when they are dealing with totals that are more than or less than 100.

Mathematics Background

The following are key ideas in developing algorithms for fractions that are continued in *Bits and Pieces III*.

Decimal Multiplication and Division

One of the first hurdles for students in their understanding of multiplication of fractions and decimals is realizing that multiplication does not always "make greater." Their experience with whole-number multiplication has firmly established this incorrect belief. In fact, multiplication involving numbers that are not whole numbers may be interpreted as an operator that may "stretch" (make greater) or "shrink" (make less) depending on whether the fraction or decimal is greater or less than one. This is a big idea that supports understanding what multiplication of fractions or decimals entails.

Models for multiplication of fractions used in the *Bits and Pieces II* unit are both partitioning and area models. An example of partitioning is: Seth is running $\frac{1}{3}$ of a $\frac{1}{2}$-mile relay race. How far will he run?

An example of an area model is: Mr. Sims asks to buy $\frac{1}{2}$ of a pan that is $\frac{2}{3}$ full. What fraction of a whole pan does Mr. Sims buy?

These models continue to be useful with decimals.

Division also has its share of conceptual difficulties. The answer to a division problem involving fractions, whether in fraction or decimal form, is not necessarily less than the dividend. Again, it depends on the size of the divisor. For example, the answer to $3 \div 0.25 = 12$ is greater than the dividend. Another example is $0.25 \div 0.4 = 0.625$. What matters is that the divisor is less than 1.

Decimal Estimation

In *Bits and Pieces I* we looked at benchmark fractions and their decimal equivalents. These fraction benchmark ideas can be used to estimate small decimal computations as well. For example, let us look at estimating the sum, the difference, the product, and the quotient of 0.78 and 0.14.

$0.78 + 0.14$ is near $\frac{3}{4} + \frac{1}{8}$ or $\frac{6}{8} + \frac{1}{8}$. So a reasonable estimate is a little less than 1 or perhaps about 0.9.

$0.78 - 0.14$ would be about $\frac{6}{8} - \frac{1}{8}$ or $\frac{5}{8}$. So a reasonable estimate is about 0.6.

0.78×0.14 would be about $\frac{6}{8} \times \frac{1}{8}$ or $\frac{6}{64}$. So a reasonable estimate is about 0.1.

$0.78 \div 0.14$ would be about $\frac{6}{8} \div \frac{1}{8}$ or about 6.

In each case estimating with benchmark fractions is helpful.

Other strategies are also useful. In the examples above, students can round to convenient decimals in their heads and estimate from these. For example, you could round 0.78 to 0.8 and 0.14 to 0.1. This rounds one number up and the other down. This would give the following mental computations with one-digit decimals to make an estimate:

> 0.78 + 0.14 is near 0.8 + 0.1 but a bit greater than 0.9.
>
> 0.78 – 0.14 would be near 0.8 – 0.1 but a bit less than 0.7.
>
> 0.78 × 0.14 would be about 0.8 × 0.1 or a bit greater than 0.08. So you might guess that the product is closer to 0.1.
>
> 0.78 ÷ 0.14 would be about 0.8 ÷ 0.1 or about 8.

Since the dividend was rounded up and the divisor was rounded down, the estimate will be too large. So we might estimate the answer to be closer to 6.

There is no "one right way to estimate" that works for every situation. Students need to build a repertoire of strategies and a sense, through experience, discussion, and analysis, of what works in a given situation.

Developing Algorithms for Computing With Decimals

As we stated earlier, students have two ways of making sense of what decimals mean. Students extend the place value system on which our number system is built, or they can interpret decimals as fractions. (Obviously these two ideas are related, but they have different looks and feels to students.) In order to have the most robust understanding of and skill with computation, students need to understand each of these meanings of decimals and be able to use them. Depending on the operation, the fraction interpretation or the place value interpretation may contribute more directly to finding shortcut algorithms. However, looking at the algorithms developed through each lens can help develop deeper understanding.

The location of a digit in a number shows the value of the digit. This is a fundamentally important concept for students. Without place value understanding, work with decimals will suffer. In the Getting Ready for Problem 1.2, students look at why it makes sense to add by examining the value of each digit and recognizing that you must be careful to add digits that represent comparable values.

Looking at the patterns in such problems as the following, (Problem 2.4) brings a *place value*

perspective to developing an algorithm for multiplication of decimals.

1. Find the following products using the fact that 21 × 11 = 231.

a. 2.1 × 11	**b.** 2.1 × 1.1
c. 2.1 × 0.11	**d.** 2.1 × 0.011
e. 0.21 × 11	**f.** 0.021 × 1.1
g. 0.021 × 0.11	**h.** 0.21 × 0.011

2. Test the algorithm you wrote in Question C on these problems.

We continue to use a combination of place value and fraction interpretations of decimals to develop a division algorithm. We also help students relate division of decimals to the long form of division of whole numbers.

Decimal Forms of Rational Numbers

Students have already observed that the decimal forms for some fractions, such as $\frac{1}{3} = 0.3333333\ldots$, "go on forever," but show a repeating pattern. Non-repeating infinite decimals such as $0.10110111011110111110\ldots$ *never* reach a point where the digits start to repeat. These are *irrational numbers*, such as π and $\sqrt{2}$, and they are not considered in this unit. They are discussed in the grade 8 unit, *Looking for Pythagoras*. Here we are interested in the decimal forms of *rational numbers*.

Some rational numbers have a finite (or terminating) decimal form. Here are some examples: $\frac{1}{2} = 0.5, \frac{3}{4} = 0.75, \frac{1}{8} = 0.125, \frac{3}{25} = 0.12$. Others have an infinite repeating decimal form, such as $\frac{2}{3} = 0.666666666\ldots, \frac{8}{15} = 0.5333333$, or $\frac{3}{7} = 0.42857142857142\ldots$

In Problem 3.5, we examine rational numbers to figure out how to predict whether a given fraction will have a repeating or terminating decimal form. Rational numbers in *simplified fraction form* that have only 2's or 5's in the prime factorization of the denominator will have a terminating decimal form, for example, $\frac{12}{75} = 0.16$. In simplified fraction form, $\frac{12}{75} = \frac{4}{25}$, which has only factors of five in the denominator. Fractions with factors other than 2's and 5's in the simplest denominator equivalent form will have a repeating decimal form, for example $\frac{13}{75} = 0.17333333\ldots$ and $\frac{4}{3} = 1.333333\ldots$

Percents

This unit uses the students' knowledge of operations with decimals to return to the uses of percents and further develops students' understanding and skill in solving percent problems. Using the relationship $a\%$ of b equals c, any one of the letters a, b, or c can be the missing value. This means that the three kinds of percent problems developed separately in some texts are looked at in context with the focus on the relationships among these three variables. The following are examples of problems students solve in the fourth investigation of this unit.

1. Jill wants to buy a CD that is priced at $7.50. The sales tax is 6%. What will be the total cost of the CD?

   In this problem, students know the price of the item and need to find 6% of the price. So here the values of a and b are known and the students must find the value of c. The equation would look like the following:

   $$6\% \text{ of } \$7.50 = c.$$

   They have to multiply 0.06×7.50 to find c.

2. Customers leave Jerome $2.50 as a tip for service. The tip is 20% of the total bill for their food. How much is the bill?

   In the equation we now have 20% of b equals $2.50 and we have to find the value of b. Solving this equation can be done in several ways. One way is to ask how many 20%'s it takes to make 100%. In this case we need five. So $5 \times \$2.50$ gives us $12.50. Later in CMP, students will have more sophisticated equation-solving techniques and will be able to think of solving a problem like this by dividing each side by 0.2 to get $b = \$12.50$.

3. At another music store, Rita gets a $12 discount off a purchase of $48. What percent discount does she get?

   In this situation our equation looks like this: $a\%$ of $48 equals $12. We have to find the percent that 12 is of 48. Students can informally solve this by asking themselves how many 12's it takes to get 48. It takes four 12's to make 48 so the percent must be $\frac{1}{4}$ of 100%. This would be 25%. As with the previous example, students will have more sophisticated solution methods later in the CMP curriculum

and can return to these types of equations and divide each side of the equation by 48 to find 0.25, or 25%, as the answer.

These informal equation-solving techniques are powerful ways of thinking that are based on understanding the situation. Work of this kind should lead to better student monitoring of their work when equation-solving techniques are more fully developed in grades 7 and 8. Rushing to techniques here may mask understanding of the problem situations and what the problem is asking.

Working Backwards

A final kind of percent situation to which students are introduced is set in a restaurant scenario in which you know the total amount of money you have. You know what percent the taxes and the tip are, but you want to figure out how much you can spend on food and still pay the bill. Here is a specific example: Your group has $60. The tax on food is 5% and you want to leave a 15% tip on the food before tax. How much can you spend on food?

The first thing to realize is that you can add together the 5% and the 15% since you are taking these percents of the same number and adding them together $(0.15x + 0.05x = 0.20x)$. If the tip were also on the tax, the situation would be more complicated.

Here is a diagram that illustrates a way of solving the problem. Since the tax and tip will be 20% of the cost of the meal, the total amount can be thought of as representing 120% and the meal cost representing 100%. This leads to partitioning the 120% bar into six equal parts, each of which is 20%. On the cost line, the six partitions show us that each 20% represents $10, so the cost of the food must not exceed $50.

Series of percent bars

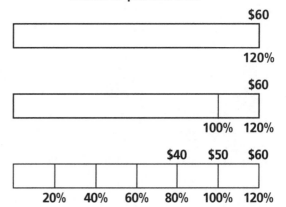

Circle Graphs

The final problem in the unit uses what students know about percents to make a new form of graphical representation for data called a circle graph. The key to a circle graph is that you know there are 360° in a full turn around the center of a circle. To represent the data, you need to figure out what angle represents the amount of turn for a certain percent of the data. One way to help students understand circle graphs is to start with small disks or other small objects, such as peas that have been colored. The total for the colors should be in different proportions. Form a circle with the objects making sure to put all the objects of one color adjacent to each other. Then draw the outline of the circle around the objects and draw lines from the center of the circle to separate the segments made by each color. This makes a rough circle graph.

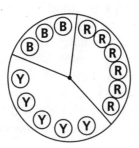

There are 14 disks in the circle. Count the number of each color. Use fractions to represent the fractional part of the data each color represents.

$$\frac{3}{14} \text{ blue}; \frac{5}{14} \text{ yellow}; \frac{6}{14} \text{ red}$$

Use the equivalent percents to multiply by 360°.

$$\frac{3}{14} \approx 21\% \text{ and } 0.21 \times 360° = 75.6°$$

$$\frac{5}{14} \approx 36\% \text{ and } 0.36 \times 360° = 129.6°$$

$$\frac{6}{14} \approx 43\% \text{ and } 0.43 \times 360° = 154.8°$$

Now make the circle graph precisely.

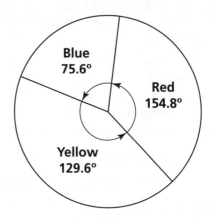

Big Idea	Prior Work	Future Work
Performing mathematical operations with decimals	Interpreting decimals as fractions; understanding place value of decimals; combining and comparing decimals (*Bits and Pieces I*); performing mathematical operations with fractions (*Bits and Pieces II*)	Interpreting decimals as probabilities (*How Likely Is It?; What Do You Expect?; Data Distributions; Samples and Populations*); interpreting decimals as scale factors, ratios, and proportions (*Stretching and Shrinking*); using decimals in scientific notation (*Data Around Us ©2004*); interpreting decimals as constants and variable coefficients in linear and nonlinear equations and relationships (*Variables and Patterns; Moving Straight Ahead; Thinking With Mathematical Models; Growing, Growing, Growing; Frogs, Fleas, and Painted Cubes; Say It With Symbols; The Shapes of Algebra*); using decimals to understand negative rational numbers (*Accentuate the Negative*)
Developing and applying algorithms for performing decimal calculations	Connecting fractions, decimals, and percents to check the reasonableness of answers, estimating to check reasonableness of answers (*Bits and Pieces I*); developing and applying algorithms for performing fraction calculations (*Bits and Pieces II*); developing algorithms for finding the area and perimeter of 2–D shapes (*Covering and Surrounding*)	Developing algorithms for finding the volume and surface area of 3–D shapes (*Filling and Wrapping*); developing algorithms for integer computation (*Accentuate the Negative*); Applying decimals in studying probability (*How Likely Is It?; What Do You Expect?; Samples and Populations*); applying ratios, proportions, and scale factors (*Stretching and Shrinking; Comparing and Scaling*)
Inverse relationships and operations in decimal settings	Inverse operations in whole-number settings (elementary school); inverse operations in fraction settings (*Bits and Pieces II*); finding an unknown dimension given area (*Covering and Surrounding*)	Inverse operations in integer settings (*Accentuate the Negative; Filling and Wrapping*); solving algebraic equations (*Moving Straight Ahead; Thinking With Mathematical Models; Say It With Symbols; The Shapes of Algebra*); patterns of change (*Moving Straight Ahead; Thinking With Mathematical Models; Growing, Growing, Growing; Frogs, Fleas, and Painted Cubes; The Shapes of Algebra*)
Performing computations involving percents	Defining, comparing, and applying percents (*Bits and Pieces I*)	Interpreting percents as probabilities (*How Likely Is It?; What Do You Expect?; Samples and Populations*); applying percents to analyze data (*Data About Us; Data Distributions*)

Pacing Suggestions and Materials

Investigations and Assessments	Pacing 45–50 min. classes	Materials for Students	Materials for Teachers
1 Decimals—More or Less!	4 days		Transparencies 1.1, 1.2, 1.3
Mathematical Reflections	$\frac{1}{2}$ day		
Assessment: Check Up 1	$\frac{1}{2}$ day		
2 Decimal Times	$5\frac{1}{2}$ days	Labsheet 2.4	Transparencies 2.1, 2.3, 2.4; Summary Transparency 2.1
Mathematical Reflections	$\frac{1}{2}$ day		
Assessment: Partner Quiz	1 day		
3 The Decimal Divide	5 days		Transparencies 3.2A, 3.2B, and 3.3
Mathematical Reflections	$\frac{1}{2}$ day		
Assessment: Check Up 2	1 day		
4 Using Percents	4 days	Labsheets 4.1, 4.2A, and 4.2B	Transparencies 4.1A and 4.1B (optional)
Mathematical Reflections	$\frac{1}{2}$ day		
5 More About Percents	$3\frac{1}{2}$ days	Labsheet 5.3; protractors or angle rulers	Transparencies 4.1B (optional) and 5.3
Mathematical Reflections	$\frac{1}{2}$ day		
Looking Back and Looking Ahead	1 day		
Assessment: Unit Project	Optional	Ordering From a Catalog, C.M. Project Catalog Order Form	
Assessment: Self Assessment	Take Home		
Assessment: Unit Test	1 day		

Total Time	29 days

Materials to Use in All Investigations	
Calculators, blank transparencies and transparency markers (optional), student notebooks	Blank transparencies and transparency markers (optional)

For detailed pacing for Problems within each Investigation, see the Suggested Pacing at the beginning of each Investigation.

For pacing with block scheduling, see next page.

Pacing for Block Scheduling (90-minute class periods)

Investigation	Suggested Pacing	Investigation	Suggested Pacing	Investigation	Suggested Pacing
Investigation 1	$2\frac{1}{2}$ **days**	**Investigation 3**	**3 days**	**Investigation 5**	$2\frac{1}{2}$ **days**
Problem 1.1	$\frac{1}{2}$ day	Problem 3.1	$\frac{1}{2}$ day	Problem 5.1	$\frac{1}{2}$ day
Problem 1.2	$\frac{1}{2}$ day	Problem 3.2	$\frac{1}{2}$ day	Problem 5.2	1 day
Problem 1.3	$\frac{1}{2}$ day	Problem 3.3	1 day	Problem 5.3	$\frac{1}{2}$ day
Problem 1.4	$\frac{1}{2}$ day	Problem 3.4	$\frac{1}{2}$ day	Math Reflections	$\frac{1}{2}$ day
Math Reflections	$\frac{1}{2}$ day	Math Reflections	$\frac{1}{2}$ day		
Investigation 2	$3\frac{1}{2}$ **days**	**Investigation 4**	**3 days**		
Problem 2.1	1 day	Problem 4.1	1 day		
Problem 2.2	$\frac{1}{2}$ day	Problem 4.2	$\frac{1}{2}$ day		
Problem 2.3	1 day	Problem 4.3	1 day		
Problem 2.4	$\frac{1}{2}$ day	Math Reflections	$\frac{1}{2}$ day		
Math Reflections	$\frac{1}{2}$ day				

Vocabulary

Essential Terms Developed in This Unit	Useful Terms Referenced in This Unit	Terms Developed in Previous Units
repeating decimal	difference	algorithm
terminating decimal	dividend	base ten
power of ten	divisor	benchmark
	factor	decimal
	mean	denominator
	product	estimate
	quotient	fact family
	sum	fraction
		mathematical sentence
		number sentence
		numerator
		percent
		place value

Program Resources

Go Online
PHSchool.com
For: Teacher Resources
Web Code: amk-5500

Components

Use the chart below to quickly see which components are available for each Investigation.

Investigation	Labsheets	Additional Practice	Transparencies		Formal Assessment		Assessment Options	
			Problem	Summary	Check Up	Partner Quiz	Multiple-Choice	Question Bank
1		✔	1.1, 1.2, 1.3		✔		✔	✔
2	2.4	✔	2.1, 2.3, 2.4	2.1		✔	✔	✔
3		✔	3.2A, 3.2B, 3.3		✔			✔
4	4.1, 4.2A, 4.2B	✔	4.1A, 4.1B		✔		✔	✔
5	5.3	✔	5.3			✔		✔
Unit Project	Ordering From a Catalog, Catalog Order Form							
For the Unit		ExamView CD-ROM, Web site	LBLA		Unit Test, Unit Project Notebook Check, Self Assessment		Multiple-Choice, Question Bank, ExamView CD-ROM	

Also Available for Use With This Unit

- Parent Guide: take-home letter for the unit
- Implementing CMP
- Spanish Assessment Resources
- Additional online and technology resources

Technology

The Use of Calculators

Connected Mathematics was developed with the belief that calculators should be available and that students should learn when their use is appropriate. For this reason, we do not designate specific problems as "calculator problems." However, in this unit, we suggest that students refrain from using calculators unless it is specifically noted to use them. Rushing to use the calculator does not promote a deep analysis of why operations work, how to compute an answer, and what an answer means.

Student Activity CD-ROM

Includes interactive activities to enhance the learning in the Problems within Investigations.

PHSchool.com

For Students Multiple-choice practice with instant feedback, updated data sources, data sets for Tinkerplots data software.

For Teachers Professional development, curriculum support, downloadable forms, and more. See also www.math.msu.edu/cmp.

ExamView® CD-ROM

Create multiple versions of practice sheets and tests for course objectives and standardized tests. Includes dynamic questions, online testing, student reports, and all test and practice items in Spanish. Also includes all items in the *Assessment Resources* and *Additional Practice*.

Teacher Express™ CD-ROM

Includes a lesson planning tool, the Teacher's Guide pages, and all the teaching resources.

LessonLab Online Courses

LessonLab offers comprehensive, facilitated professional development designed to help teachers implement CMP2 and improve student achievement. To learn more, please visit PHSchool.com/cmp2.

Ongoing Informal Assessment

Embedded in the Student Unit

Problems Use students' work from the Problems to check student understanding.

ACE exercises Use ACE exercises for homework assignments to assess student understanding.

Mathematical Reflections Have students summarize their learning at the end of each Investigation.

Looking Back and Looking Ahead At the end of the unit, use the first two sections to allow students to show what they know about the unit.

Additional Resources

Teacher's Edition Use the Check for Understanding feature of some Summaries and the probing questions that appear in the *Launch, Explore,* or *Summarize* sections of all Investigations to check student understanding.

Summary Transparencies Use these transparencies to focus class attention on a summary check for understanding.

Self Assessment

Notebook Check Students use this tool to organize and check their notebooks before giving them to their teacher. Located in *Assessment Resources*.

Self Assessment At the end of the unit, students reflect on and provide examples of what they learned. Located in *Assessment Resources*.

Formal Assessment

Choose the assessment materials that are appropriate for your students

Assessment	For Use After	Focus	Student Work
Check Up 1	Invest. 1	Skills	Individual
Partner Quiz	Invest. 2	Skills	Pair
Check Up 2	Invest. 3	Rich problems	Individual
Unit Test	The Unit	Skills, rich problems	Individual
Unit Project	The Unit	Rich problems	Ind./Pair

Additional Resources

Multiple-Choice Items Use these items for homework, review, a quiz, or add them to the Unit Test.

Question Bank Choose from these questions for homework, review, or replacements for Quiz, Check Up, or Unit Test questions.

Additional Practice Choose practice exercises for each Investigation for homework, review, or formal assessments.

ExamView **CD-ROM** Create practice sheets, review quizzes, and tests with this dynamic software. Give online tests and receive student progress reports. *(All test items are also available in Spanish.)*

Spanish Assessment Resources

Includes Partner Quizzes, Check Ups, Unit Test, Multiple-Choice Items, Question Bank, Notebook Check, and Self Assessment. Plus, the *ExamView* CD-ROM has all test items in Spanish.

Correlation to Standardized Tests

Investigation	NAEP	Terra Nova				Local Test
		CAT6	CTBS	ITBS	SAT10	
1 Decimals—More or Less!	N2b, N3a, M2b	✔	✔	✔	✔	
2 Decimal Times	N3a, N3d, N3f	✔	✔	✔	✔	
3 The Decimal Divide	N3a, N3d, N3f	✔	✔	✔	✔	
4 Using Percents	N3a, N3g, N4d	✔	✔	✔	✔	
5 More About Percents	N3g, N4d, D1b	✔	✔	✔	✔	

NAEP National Assessment of Educational Progress

CAT6/Terra Nova California Achievement Test, 6th Ed.
CTBS/Terra Nova Comprehensive Test of Basic Skills

ITBS Iowa Test of Basic Skills, Form M
SAT10 Stanford Achievement Test, 10th Ed.

Using the Unit Opener

Discuss the questions posed on the opening page of the Student Edition, which are designed to start students thinking about the kinds of questions and mathematics in the unit. Don't look for "correct" answers at this time. Do, however, present an opportunity for the class to discuss the questions and to start to think about what is needed to answer them. You may want to revisit these questions as students learn the mathematical ideas and techniques necessary to find the answers.

This would also be an appropriate time to talk with your class about the role of calculators in this unit. Talk to them about the work they will be doing including developing estimation strategies and algorithms or procedures for being able to add, subtract, multiply and divide with decimals. In general, unless a problem indicates that this is appropriate, calculators should not be used.

Many of the decimal skills and concepts developed in this unit ask students to draw upon their knowledge of fractions and decimal–fraction relationships. It may be beneficial to your students to spend part of a class period playing the Getting Close Game from *Bits and Pieces II*.

Using the Mathematical Highlights

The Mathematical Highlights page in the Student Edition provides information to students, parents, and other family members. It gives students a preview of the mathematics and some of the overarching questions that they should ask themselves while studying *Bits and Pieces III*.

As they work through the unit, students can refer back to the Mathematical Highlights page to review what they have learned and to preview what is still to come. This page also tells students' families what mathematical ideas and activities will be covered as the class works through *Bits and Pieces III*.

Using the Unit Project

The optional unit project, Ordering From a Catalog, allows students to apply what they have learned about decimals and percents while they dream about things that they would like to order from a catalog.

The project has two parts. In part I, students are asked to select three items from a catalog and fill out an order blank as if they were going to purchase the items. They must find shipping cost (which is a percent of the total cost) and the sales tax (based on the rate for their state). They are also asked to compute what the items would cost if given discounts were applied. In part II, students are asked to work backwards to find the maximum cost of the three items so that Uri would be able to pay the tax and shipping as well. They are also asked to find three items that would come closest to the $125 Uri got for his birthday.

The blackline masters for the order blank appear on page 126. Depending on the time you have for students to work on the project, you may choose to only assign part I. You may find it helpful to begin collecting catalogs a few weeks before assigning the project. This will provide options for students who do not have catalogs available at home.

A scoring rubric and samples of student work are given on pages 117–119.

Connected Mathematics 2™

Bits and Pieces III

Computing With Decimals and Percents

Glenda Lappan

James T. Fey

William M. Fitzgerald

Susan N. Friel

Elizabeth Difanis Phillips

PEARSON

Boston, Massachusetts · Glenview, Illinois · Shoreview, Minnesota · Upper Saddle River, New Jersey

STUDENT PAGE

Notes _____

_____

_____

_____

Bits and Pieces III

Computing With Decimals and Percents

Shing is helping his brother, Chi, with his math homework. Shing says that to multiply a number by 10, you just add a zero to it. What do you think he means? Is he correct? What mistake do you think Chi might make when he tries to use Shing's rule?

Mrs. Doran takes her three grandchildren out to lunch. Each grandchild orders a meal that costs $2.95. What is the cost of the three meals?

★ Kids' Menu ★

Chicken Nuggets . . $2.95
P.B. & J. $2.95
Hot Dog $2.95
Mac & Cheese $2.95

Lisa buys a hat for $27.00 that originally cost $36.00. What percent has the hat been marked down?

Notes _____

_____

_____

_____

In *Bits and Pieces II*, you studied the operations of addition, subtraction, multiplication, and division with fractions. In this unit, you will study the same operations with decimals. You will need to decide which operation makes sense in each situation.

Knowing how to estimate and to compute with all kinds of numbers is important. You already know about working with fractions and with whole numbers. In this unit, you will use what you know to make sense of, and find shortcuts for, computing with decimal numbers.

You will then use all of this knowledge to develop strategies for working with percents in everyday situations.

Remember, finding the right answers is only one part of your work in math. You must also be able to make sense of and describe your strategies for finding these answers.

Notes _____

_____

_____

_____

Mathematical Highlights

Computing With Decimals and Percents

In *Bits and Pieces III*, you will learn how to perform and make sense of the four operations (+, −, ×, ÷) on decimal numbers. You will improve your understanding and skill in working with percents.

You will learn how to

- Use your knowledge of fractions to learn about operating on decimals
- Estimate the results of operations on decimals
- Use your knowledge of place value in working with decimals
- Know when to use each operation in a situation involving decimals
- Recognize real-world situations where people often choose to use decimals instead of common fractions
- Develop algorithms for solving a variety of types of percent problems

As you work on problems in this unit, ask yourself questions about situations that involve decimals and percents:

What is the whole (unit) in this situation?

How big are the numbers in this problem?

About how large will the sum be?

About how large will the difference be?

About how large will the product be?

About how large will the quotient be?

How do these decimals compare to fractions that I know?

Why are percents useful in this problem?

Notes _____

_____

_____

_____

Investigation 1 — Decimals—More or Less!

Mathematical and Problem-Solving Goals

- Use benchmarks and decimal-fraction relationships to develop estimation strategies for finding decimal sums

- Consider the relative size of a decimal prior to developing approaches to finding exact decimal sums or differences

- Develop place-value understanding of decimal addition and subtraction

- Develop strategies for adding and subtracting decimal numbers

- Solve problems that require decimal addition and subtraction

- Connect strategies for addition and subtraction of decimals to addition and subtraction of fractions with powers of ten in the denominator

- Relate renaming fractions to have common denominators to the notion of adding values with the same place value

- Develop and use efficient algorithms for adding and subtracting decimals

- Explore the inverse relationship between addition and subtraction in decimal settings

Summary of Problems

Problem 1.1 About How Much?

Students build on addition-subtraction fraction estimation work in *Bits and Pieces II* to estimate with adding and subtracting decimals.

Problem 1.2 Adding and Subtracting Decimals

Problem 1.2 develops a place-value understanding of decimal addition and subtraction computation.

Problem 1.3 Using Fractions to Add and Subtract Decimals

Students relate a place-value approach to addition and subtraction of decimals to fraction addition and subtraction. The place-value approach helps them to understand and develop strategies for adding and subtracting with decimals.

Problem 1.4 Decimal Sum and Difference Algorithms

Students write an algorithm for finding decimal sums and differences. They use inverse operations of addition and subtraction to develop fact families and solve missing value problems.

Mathematics Background

For background on estimation and computation of sums and differences, see pages 5–6.

	Suggested Pacing	Materials for Students	Materials for Teachers	ACE Assignments
All	$4\frac{1}{2}$ days			
1.1	1 day		Transparency 1.1	1–7, 37–38
1.2	1 day	Chart paper or blank transparency film, markers (optional)	Transparency 1.2	8–18, 39, 47, 48
1.3	1 day		Transparency 1.3	19–22, 40–44, 49–52
1.4	1 day	Chart paper or blank transparency film, markers (optional)		23–36, 45, 46, 53–58
MR	$\frac{1}{2}$ day			

1.1 About How Much?

Goals

- Use benchmarks and decimal-fraction relationships to develop estimation strategies for finding decimal sums
- Consider the relative size of a decimal prior to developing approaches to finding exact decimal sums or differences

Launch 1.1

Have a conversation with the students about estimating and benchmarks. Revisit the fraction-decimal benchmarks that were developed in *Bits and Pieces I*. The number line before the Getting Ready contains "quarter" benchmarks. Students may point out or draw upon additional benchmarks previously developed. Ask them about where the additional benchmarks belong on the number line in relation to the benchmarks that are already there.

Suggested Questions Ask:

- *In this problem you will look at shopping and money situations where estimation is used. Why do people estimate when they shop?*

Use the Getting Ready to talk about estimation strategies. This will prepare the students for the tasks in the problem. Read through the situation with students, provide a few minutes for students to work on the Tat Ming problem, and then discuss their solutions. Focus on students' estimation strategies.

- *What is Tat Ming making for his friends?* (Nachos)

- *Does Tat Ming have enough money to pay for the groceries?* (Yes)

- *Without computing an exact answer, how can you be sure whether Tat Ming has enough money to pay for his groceries?* (One strategy is to add the whole number amounts first. This gives $7, so you still have $3. If you take 2

pennies from the $0.79 left for the chips you can make $2 from the cents left from the chips, salsa, and cheese and have $0.07 left. The sum of $0.12, $0.45, and $0.07 is less than a dollar, so he has enough to pay his bill. Another strategy is to round to benchmarks. Chips: $2.75, Salsa: $2.00, Cheese: $1.25; Ground Beef: $3.25; Jalapenos: $0.50; Total: $9.75.)

- *If you round to the nearest benchmark, and some values are increased and others decreased, how do you know if he will have enough money?* (The amount rounded up to get the estimate for ground beef and jalapenos is more than the amount rounded down for the other items. The estimate will still be more than the actual cost, but less than $10.)

- *What would be the exact cost of Tat Ming's groceries?* ($9.64)

Read through the first question with the students to be sure they understand what they are expected to do. This is a good problem for a Think-Pair-Share arrangement.

Explore 1.1

As you circulate, look for students who are having trouble deciding where a decimal number fits within a set of benchmarks. Suggest that they draw pictures, draw upon fraction benchmarks, or think about a number line and the number's location on the number line as an aid to figuring out where the decimal fits.

Look for students who have unique and interesting ways to estimate sums and differences. At this point it is not important to develop or identify an efficient strategy or algorithm. The focus should stay on questions such as, "About how great is this decimal?" or "If I add or subtract two given decimals, about how much is the sum or difference?"

Summarize 1.1

Have students share their solutions to Question A, parts (1)–(3), focusing on how they made their estimates.

Suggested Questions Ask:

- *How did you decide if Nick had enough money to buy everything he wanted?*

- *How would you describe your estimation strategy?* (Possible descriptions might include rounding to the nearest dollar or rounding to the next highest "quarter" benchmark.)

- *Is your estimate an underestimate or overestimate of the actual cost?*

Now move to part (4) of Question A. As students offer solutions, focus on how they knew the price of the items they chose led to spending as much of the $10 as possible.

Call on someone to describe how he or she solved Question B about Maria. Ask if other students thought about the problem differently. For Question C, discuss the various strategies students have for estimating with decimals as money.

Suggested Questions Ask:

- *Did you use this strategy on every number or did you sometimes think in a different way?*

- *What do you think of _____'s strategy? Does it seem reasonable? When would you use this strategy?*

- *If you want a close overestimate, what strategies could you use? Why?* (Round up the quantities to the nearest benchmarks. You could round a quantity down if it is close to a fraction or decimal benchmark and you have rounded another number up by at least that much. You could also combine values that are easy to add in your head and estimate the rest.)

- *If you want a close underestimate, what strategies could you use? Why?* (Round down quantities to the nearest benchmark. You could round a quantity up if it is close to a fraction or decimal benchmark and you have rounded another number down by at least that much. You could also combine values that are easy to add in your head and estimate the rest.)

- *Did you use rounding to the nearest dollar? If so, when and why?* (When the numbers were close to a whole number amount. If there was one number that was greater than a whole number amount and one slightly less than a whole, I rounded one up and one down to compensate.)

- *Did you estimate with quarter amounts or tenths? If so, when and why?*

Some students prefer to always overestimate with money while others may at times use a system of checks and balances. For example, if they have rounded up for two amounts and the third amount is close to a lower benchmark, they might round down instead of up.

Look for strategies students are using to estimate sums or differences with decimals. Benchmarking to $0, \frac{1}{4}, \frac{1}{2}, \frac{3}{4}$, and 1 is very powerful. Be sure that this strategy is on the table.

Mathematical Goals

- Use benchmarks and decimal-fraction relationships to develop estimation strategies for finding decimal sums
- Consider the relative size of a decimal prior to developing approaches to finding exact decimal sums or differences

Launch

Revisit the fraction-decimal benchmarks that were developed in *Bits and Pieces I*. The number line before the Getting Ready contains "quarter" benchmarks.

Students may point out or draw upon additional benchmarks previously developed. Ask where the additional benchmarks belong on the number line.

- *In this problem you will look at shopping and money situations where estimation is used. Why do people estimate when they shop?*

Use the Getting Ready to talk about estimation strategies and prepare students for the tasks in the problem. Read through the situation with students, provide a few minutes for students to work on the Tat Ming problem, and then discuss their solutions. Focus on students' estimation strategies.

- *Does Tat Ming have enough money to pay for the groceries?*
- *Without computing an exact answer, how can you be sure whether Tat Ming has enough money to pay for his groceries?*
- *What would be the exact cost of Tat Ming's groceries?*

Read through Problem 1.1 with students to be sure they understand what is expected. This is a good problem for a Think-Pair-Share arrangement.

Materials
- Transparency 1.1

Explore

For students who are having trouble deciding where a decimal number fits within a set of benchmarks, suggest they draw pictures, draw upon fraction benchmarks, or think about a number line and the number's location on the number line. Look for students who have unique and interesting ways to estimate.

Summarize

Have students share their solutions to Question A parts (1)–(3), focusing on how they made their estimates.

- *How did you decide if Nick had enough money to buy everything he wanted?*
- *How would you describe your estimation strategy?*

Materials
- Student notebooks

continued on next page

continued

For part (4) of Question A, focus on how they knew the price of the items they chose led to spending as much of the $10 as possible. For Question B, call on someone to describe his or her solution. Ask if other students thought about the problem differently. For Question C, discuss the various strategies students have for estimating with decimals as money.

 • *When would you use this strategy?*

Look for strategies students are using to estimate sums or differences with decimals. Benchmarking to $0, \frac{1}{4}, \frac{1}{2}, \frac{3}{4}$, and 1 is very powerful. Be sure that this strategy is on the table.

ACE Assignment Guide for Problem 1.1

Core 1–6, 37–38
Other *Applications* 7

Adapted For suggestions about adapting ACE exercises, see the CMP *Special Needs Handbook*.
Connecting to Prior Units 37–38: *Bit and Pieces I*

Answers to Problem 1.1

A. **1.** A little more than $13.

  2. With the game included, Nick will not have enough money.

  3. Overestimate. Your total estimate should be more than the actual cost and allow you to be sure the actual total is less than $20.

  4. Nick will spend as close to $10 as possible if he buys the game and the basketball cards. $6.89 + $2.89 = $9.78

B. Maria will have $73 after she pays her brother. With Grandmother's gift she will have nearly $100. With the $10 from baby sitting and the $13.73 from the piggy bank, she will have slightly less than $125. Even if she makes the extra $2 from babysitting, she will not have enough to get the bike next week.

C. Possible strategies: Round to nearest benchmark fraction, round some quantities up and others down. (Some students may discuss when an underestimate or an overestimate is appropriate and its relationship to the exact answer.)

1.2 Adding and Subtracting Decimals

Goals

- Develop place-value understanding of decimal addition and subtraction

- Develop strategies for adding and subtracting decimal numbers

- Solve problems that require decimal addition and subtraction

Our intent with this problem is to help students draw upon what they know about place value and money to develop strategies for adding or subtracting decimals. Students may need to review decimal place value. Throughout this problem and others in the unit, it will be helpful if students use the correct place value name when discussing decimals. For example, encourage the use of "3 and 2 tenths" as opposed to "3 point 2."

Launch 1.2

Use the Getting Ready to launch the problem. Here you have a careless clerk that makes an error in a bill. A quick estimate of the cost of the items bought suggests that the bill is not correct. The challenge for the students is to try to figure out what the clerk did to make the error. The frazzled clerk forgot place value! Use the place value chart and other examples to review place value and to make the point that it makes no sense to add digits together that do not represent the same size quantities.

Suggested Questions Ask:

- *The cash register in the express lane is broken and the clerk says the bill (before taxes) is $10.87. Do you agree? If not, explain what the clerk probably did wrong.* (The clerk is incorrect because the cider is less than two dollars and the pretzels are less than one dollar. The total cannot be more than three dollars. The clerk might have added the wrong digits together.)

$$\begin{array}{r} 1.97 \\ +\ .89 \\ \hline \$10.87 \end{array}$$

- *Why is it an error to add the 8 in the price of the pretzels to the 1 in the price of the cider?* (The "1" means "one dollar" while the "8" means "8 dimes." We cannot add one dollar and eight dimes to get nine dollars.)

When students are comfortable with the structure of place value with decimals, use the description of the situation in the text to help students understand the context and the kinds of problems they will be solving. If you have a trundle wheel or even a round object that can be rolled to illustrate how a trundle wheel works, take a few minutes to show the students.

Remind students to write mathematical sentences using decimal notation to show their computation. They are to start a table that will also be used in Problem 1.3 to make a comparison.

Use pairs or small groups to work on the tasks posed. You may want to plan a mini-summary after Question A to be sure students are making progress on developing a strategy for adding or subtracting decimals using place value to guide the work.

Explore 1.2

As you circulate, check to see if students have their tables set up and are writing mathematical sentences in decimal notation to show their work.

Ask questions of group members to be sure they understand how to interpret digits to the right of the decimal point. Ask a group member to explain why place value is important when you are adding decimals.

Notice strategies that students are using to add or subtract decimals. Some may be thinking of the quantities as fractions. This is okay and will be the focus in the next problem. However, it is important that each student can tell the value of each digit in a decimal. Fraction form with a power of ten in the denominator is a useful way to make sense of and keep place value in the forefront.

Since students will be comparing their solutions on Problem 1.2A and Problem 1.3A, we suggest students record their solutions on chart paper or transparency film.

Summarize 1.2

Call on groups to describe how they solved each problem in Question A. Ask why these strategies make sense. For example, a group of students gave the following explanations of part (1):

> We realized that this was a subtraction problem. We looked at Carmela's goal of 1.5 miles and said that the 0.5 means 5 tenths of a mile. So we knew she had to clean a mile and a half. Then we looked at how far she got before the rain. She cleaned 25 hundredths of a mile before the rain. Since 5 tenths and 50 hundredths are the same amount, we wrote this number sentence:
> 1.50 − 0.25 = 1.25 miles left to clean.

Another student said he could see it better if it was written vertically:

$$\begin{array}{r} 1.5 \\ -\ 0.25 \\ \hline 1.25 \end{array}$$

You can see that 1.5 means 1 whole plus 5 tenths (1 + 0.5) and 0.25 is 2 tenths plus 5 hundredths (0.2 + 0.05). Written vertically, you can line up the decimals and the same place values in order to subtract.

Ask questions about what each place in each number means. Write these problems on the board and ask why they are not correct:

$$\begin{array}{r} 1.5 \\ -\ .25 \\ \hline -\ 1.0 \end{array} \qquad \begin{array}{r} 1.5 \\ -\ 0.25 \\ \hline 1.35 \end{array}$$

Call on students to talk about parts (2)–(4) as well.

Shift the conversation toward Question B part (1). Students do not have to develop a formal algorithm at this point. Use this opportunity to get them thinking about an algorithm and to push them to talk about why they need to line up the decimal points.

Here is a conversation that occurred in a classroom:

Classroom Dialog Model

Teacher *If you wanted to describe a strategy for adding and subtracting decimal numbers, what would you say?*

Torie *First you line up the decimal place.*

Teacher *Why does lining up the decimal point matter?*

Torie *Because you want to line up the whole numbers, tenths, hundredths, thousandths, and so on.*

Teacher *Okay, could we say that it lines up the place values?*

Torie *Yes. Now you add like you normally do and put the decimal in the answer so the place values stay lined up in the answer, too.*

Use the problems in Question B part (2) to test the suggested strategy or strategies. Part 2e is an important case. Here students need to add a zero to the thousandths place of 4.32 in order to borrow when they subtract the digit in the thousandths place of 1.746.

- *Keegan says that he can subtract the 6 in 1.746 from 4.32 if he rewrites 4.32 as 4.320. Can he do that?* (Yes, 4.32 and 4.320 are equivalent.)

1.2 Adding and Subtracting Decimals

Mathematical Goals

- Develop place-value understanding of decimal addition and subtraction
- Develop strategies for adding and subtracting decimal numbers
- Solve problems that require decimal addition and subtraction

Launch

Use the Getting Ready to launch the problem. A quick estimate of the cost of the items bought suggests that the bill is not correct. Use the place value chart and other examples to review place value and to make the point that it makes no sense to add digits together that do not represent the same size quantities.

When students see the structure of place value with decimals, go over Problem 1.2 with the students so they understand the context and kinds of problems they will be solving. Remind students to make a table and write mathematical sentences using decimal notation to show their computation.

Use pairs or small groups to work on the tasks posed. You may want to plan a mini-summary after Question A to be sure students are making progress on developing a strategy for adding or subtracting decimals using place value to guide the work.

Materials
- Transparency 1.2

Explore

As you circulate, check to see if students have their tables set up and are writing mathematical sentences in decimal notation to show their work.

Ask questions of group members to be sure they understand how to interpret digits to the right of the decimal point. Ask a group member to explain why place value is important when you are adding decimals.

Since students will be comparing solutions for Problems 1.2 Question A and 1.3 Question A, we suggest they record solutions on chart paper or transparency film.

Materials
- Chart paper, or blank transparency film
- Markers

Summarize

Call on groups to describe how they solved each problem in Question A. Ask why these strategies make sense. Ask questions about what each place in each number means. Call on students to talk about parts (2)–(4) as well.

Shift the conversation toward Question B part (1). Students do not have to develop a formal algorithm at this point. Use this opportunity to get them thinking about an algorithm and to talk about why they need to line up the decimal points.

Materials
- Student notebooks

continued on next page

Summarize

continued

Use the problems in Question B part (2) to test the suggested strategy(s). Part 2(c) is an important case. Students need to add a zero to the thousandths place of 4.32 in order to borrow when they subtract the digit in the thousandths place of 1.746.

- *Keegan says that he can subtract the 6 in 1.746 from 4.32 if he rewrites 4.32 as 4.320. Can he do that?*

ACE Assignment Guide for Problem 1.2

Differentiated Instruction
Solutions for All Learners

Core 8–18
Other *Connections* 39; *Extensions* 47, 48; unassigned choices from previous problems

Adapted For suggestions about adapting ACE exercises, see the CMP *Special Needs Handbook*.
Connecting to Prior Units 39: *Covering and Surrounding*

Answers to Problem 1.2

A. 1. $1.5 - 0.25 = 1.25$ miles left to clean.

2. $0.25 + 0.375 = 0.625$ cleaned altogether

3. $0.287 + 0.02 = 0.307$ cleaned.

4. Teri cleaned $0.85 + 0.005 = 0.855$ miles. She is not correct. She added 5 thousandths to 5 hundredths and got a tenth.

B. 1. Place value determines what digits can be added or subtracted. You cannot add a digit in the tenths place to a digit in the hundredths place because they have different values.

2. a. 131.1

b. 1.65

c. 4.001

d. 32.793

e. 2.574

f. 0.782

1.3 Using Fractions to Add and Subtract Decimals

Goals

- Connect strategies for addition and subtraction of decimals to addition and subtraction of fractions with powers of ten in the denominator

- Relate renaming fractions to have common denominators to the notion of adding values with the same place value

  Most students will understand decimals as special fractions from *Bits and Pieces I*. Problem 1.3 asks students to move back and forth between fraction and decimal representation for quantities in order to better understand why it makes sense to line up the decimal points when adding and subtracting decimals.

Launch 1.3

In this problem, students solve the same problems they did in Problem 1.2 but in a different form. Here we want students to work with decimals represented as fractions with powers of ten in the denominator.

Use the Getting Ready to revisit writing decimals as fractions and introduce the idea of using fraction addition and subtraction.

Students will need the table they started in Problem 1.2. Read through the problem making sure the students understand what to do. Have students work in pairs or small groups.

Explore 1.3

As students work, circulate to see whether students are using powers of ten in the denominator of their fractions or using fractions that do not have powers of ten in the denominator, for example, 0.25 for $\frac{1}{4}$. Bring both cases out in the summary. Check to see that students transition from using equivalent fractions for decimals to using fraction benchmarks and estimation in Question C.

When everyone seems to have caught on to how to think about adding or subtracting decimals using fractions, move to the summary. Any questions not done in class can be assigned as homework.

Summarize 1.3

Discuss Question A. Display the fraction solutions next to the decimal solutions from Problem 1.2. Be sure that several examples of the fraction version of the problem are demonstrated along with the decimal version. Here is one example for Question A part (2).

We can write 0.25 as $\frac{25}{100}$ and 0.375 as $\frac{375}{1,000}$. To add, rewrite the fractions with common denominators.

$$\frac{25}{100} + \frac{375}{1,000} \rightarrow \frac{250}{1,000} + \frac{375}{1,000} = \frac{625}{1,000} \text{ or } 0.625$$

Pam cleaned $\frac{1}{4}$ of a mile plus $\frac{3}{8}$ of a mile. Together she has cleaned $\frac{1}{4} + \frac{3}{8}$ of a mile. In a sentence this would be written as:

$\frac{1}{4} + \frac{3}{8} = \frac{2}{8} + \frac{3}{8} = \frac{5}{8}$ of a mile. $\frac{5}{8}$ is equal to 0.625 as a decimal. As a decimal this addition would look like: 0.25 + 0.375 = 0.625 of a mile. If we write this problem vertically, we would have this:

$$\begin{array}{rcl} \frac{1}{4} & = & 0.25 \\ + \frac{3}{8} & = & +0.375 \\ \hline \frac{5}{8} & = & 0.625 \text{ mile} \end{array}$$

These approaches help show that decimal form and fraction form lead to the same solution. Use discussion of fraction form as an opportunity to review fraction addition and subtraction.

Suggested Questions Ask:

- *How did you know a fraction for 0.375?* (If you read the decimal using place value it says 0 and 375 thousandths. As a fraction that is $\frac{375}{1,000}$.)

- *Why did you rewrite the $\frac{25}{100}$ in the problem $\frac{25}{100} + \frac{375}{1,000}$ as $\frac{250}{1,000}$?* (You need common denominators to add fractions.)

- *Why do you need common denominators?* (So both fractions are made out of the same size parts of the whole.)

- *How did you change $\frac{25}{100}$ to $\frac{250}{1,000}$? (I multiplied the numerator and the denominator by 10 so $\frac{25}{100}$ would be out of 1,000.)*
- *How is fraction form like decimal form when adding or subtracting decimals?*

Students may need support trying to answer this last question. It is the focus of Question B.

Here is a conversation about $0.25 + 0.375$ that took place in a classroom:

Classroom Dialogue Model

Brian *When you place a zero at the end of the decimal 0.25 (renaming 0.25 as 0.250), the denominator of the fraction changes from hundredths to thousandths, but it is still the same fraction in value.*

Teacher *So when you place a zero on the end of 0.25 to get 0.250, that is the same as renaming $\frac{25}{100}$ as $\frac{250}{1,000}$?*

Brian *Yes. They are equivalent. Placing a zero on the end of 0.25 renames the decimal so it is 250 thousandths instead of 25 hundredths.*

Move to question C and have students share the fraction benchmark number sentences they wrote to estimate the sums and differences. End the summary by returning to the strategies written in Problem 1.2 for adding and subtracting decimals.

Suggested Question Ask:

- *How would you explain to someone how to use fractions to add and subtract decimals?*

1.3 Using Fractions to Add and Subtract Decimals

Mathematical Goals

- Connect strategies for addition and subtraction of decimals to addition and subtraction of fractions with powers of ten in the denominator
- Relate renaming fractions to have common denominators to the notion of adding values with the same place value

Launch

In this problem students solve the same problems they did in Problem 1.2 but in a different form. Here we want students to work with decimals represented as fractions with powers of ten in the denominator. Use the Getting Ready to revisit writing decimals as fractions and introduce the idea of using fraction addition and subtraction.

Students will need the table they started in Problem 1.2. Read through the problem making sure the students understand what to do. Have students work in pairs.

Materials
- Transparency 1.3

Explore

As students work, circulate and look to see whether students are using powers of ten in the denominator of their fractions. (For example, $\frac{25}{100}$ or 0.25 for $\frac{1}{4}$.) Bring cases with and without powers of ten out in the summary. Check to see that students transition from using equivalent fractions for decimals to using fraction benchmarks and estimation in Question C.

Summarize

Discuss Question A. Display the fraction solutions next to the decimal solutions from Problem 1.2.

Use discussion of fraction form as an opportunity to review fraction addition and subtraction.

- *How did you know a fraction for 0.375?*
- *Why did you rewrite the $\frac{25}{100}$ in the problem $\frac{25}{100} + \frac{375}{1,000}$ as $\frac{250}{1,000}$?*
- *Why do you need common denominators?*
- *How did you change $\frac{25}{100}$ to $\frac{250}{1,000}$?*
- *How is fraction form like decimal form when adding or subtracting decimals?*

Students may need support with this last question, which is the focus of Question B.

Materials
- Student notebooks

continued on next page

For question C, have students share the fraction benchmark number sentences. End the summary by returning to the strategies written in Problem 1.2 for adding and subtracting decimals.

- *How would you explain to someone how to use fractions to add and subtract decimals?*

ACE Assignment Guide for Problem 1.3

Differentiated Instruction
Solutions for All Learners

Core 19–21
Other *Applications* 22, *Connections* 40–44, *Extensions* 49–52; unassigned choices from previous problems

Adapted For suggestions about adapting Exercise 20 and other ACE exercises, see the CMP *Special Needs Handbook.*
Connecting to Prior Units 40–43: *Shapes and Designs,* and *Covering and Surrounding;* 44: *Covering and Surrounding*

Answers to Problem 1.3

A. 1. $1\frac{5}{10} - \frac{25}{100} = 1\frac{50}{100} - \frac{25}{100} = 1\frac{25}{100}$, which is 1.25.

2. $\frac{25}{100} + \frac{375}{1,000} = \frac{250}{1,000} + \frac{375}{1,000} = \frac{625}{1,000}$, which is 0.625.

3. $\frac{287}{1,000} + \frac{2}{100} = \frac{287}{1,000} + \frac{20}{1,000} = \frac{307}{1,000}$, which is 0.307.

4. $\frac{85}{100} + \frac{5}{1,000} = \frac{850}{1,000} + \frac{5}{1,000} = \frac{855}{1,000}$ or 0.855, which does not equal $\frac{9}{10}$.

B. Whether you use a fraction interpretation or a place value interpretation, you get the same answer. When you rewrite fractions to have common denominators, that is similar to adding the same place values together.

C. Possible estimates that use fraction benchmarks.

1. $1\frac{2}{10} + 2 = 3\frac{2}{10}$ or 3.2

2. $1\frac{3}{4} + 7 = 8\frac{3}{4}$ or 8.75

3. $\frac{1}{4} + \frac{3}{4} = 1$

4. $3\frac{3}{4} - \frac{1}{2} = 3\frac{1}{4}$

5. $6\frac{9}{10} - 2\frac{9}{10} = 4$

6. $7\frac{1}{2} - 1 = 6\frac{1}{2}$

Decimal Sum and Difference Algorithms

Goals

- Develop and use algorithms for adding and subtracting decimals

- Explore the inverse relationship between addition and subtraction in decimal settings

   Your students have had experience with developing algorithms, inverse relationships in fact families, and solving missing value problems in *Bits and Pieces II*. This problem visits those same ideas but with decimals. For a detailed discussion of fact families and inverse relationships, see the Mathematics Background on page 12 in *Bits and Pieces II*. Like the work in *Bits and Pieces II*, we are not trying to develop formal procedures or notation for solving algebraic problems. Rather, the focus is on understanding and using inverse relationships.

Launch 1.4

Remind students of the work they have done with decimals and fractions. Talk with the class about what an algorithm is in mathematics.

Suggested Question Ask:

- *Can someone explain what an algorithm is?* (It is a plan or series of steps for doing a computation that can be used in many situations.)

   Look at the algorithm for adding fractions developed in *Bits and Pieces II*. Once students are comfortable with what an algorithm is, read through the questions in Problem 1.4. Have students work individually on Question A, then work in pairs or small groups to discuss their algorithms.

Explore 1.4

Have students record their final algorithms on transparency film or chart paper to share with the class. As students work with fact families and missing-value problems, note whether or not students are focusing on the relationship between addition and subtraction. For example, do

students use the idea that the sum in an addition problem will be the amount from which you subtract (minuend) in a subtraction problem? For $a + b = c$, the related subtraction problems are $c - b = a$ and $c - a = b$. Note that these are in the form: addend + addend = sum and sum − addend = other addend.

Summarize 1.4

Have students share their algorithms for adding and subtracting fractions. It is helpful to have students demonstrate how their algorithm works on a problem.

Suggested Questions With both fraction and decimal place-value approaches, have students talk about why their algorithm works.

- *Why do we need to line up the decimal points?* (Lining up decimal points will line up the digits with the same place value.)

- *Can someone describe what the decimal approach and the fraction approach have in common?* (With decimals, you line the tenths with tenths, hundredths with hundredths, and so on. With fractions, you rename the quantities so they are out of the same place value; for example, out of 100 or out of 10.)

- *Let's try this algorithm on this problem.* (Give an appropriate problem.) *Does it work? Does it account for all the things you have to think about to solve this problem?*

   The class does not have to develop only one algorithm, but students should have an algorithm that they can explain and use.

   With Question C, focus on the strategies students used to determine the value of N. Look for opportunities to discuss how a fact family can be helpful.

   Question D asks students to work a problem that combines fractions and decimals. One possibility is to rewrite $2\frac{1}{8}$ as a decimal, making the problem $4.27 - 2.125$. Another possibility is to rewrite 4.27 as a fraction, $4\frac{27}{100}$. Then you need to rename $2\frac{1}{8}$ as a fraction with a power of ten in the denominator.

- *Can someone share how they used decimals to subtract 4.27 − $2\frac{1}{8}$?* (I rewrote $\frac{1}{8}$ as the decimal 0.125. This led to the problem 4.27 − 2.125.)

- *How do you know that $\frac{1}{8}$ is equivalent to 0.125?* (An eighth is half of a fourth, so half of 0.25 is 0.125.)

- *Did someone use fractions to solve the problem?* (I changed 0.27 or "twenty-seven hundredths" to $\frac{27}{100}$. Then I realized that I had to rewrite $\frac{1}{8}$ as a fraction with a power of ten in the denominator.)

- *How did you do that?* (I thought of $\frac{1}{8}$ as a decimal, 0.125, then I changed the decimal to the fraction $\frac{125}{1,000}$. I had to think of the decimal form in order to find the fraction with a power of ten.)

- *Why is that?* (To change a fraction to a decimal you have to find an equivalent fraction with a power of ten in the denominator. If you want a fraction to be a power of ten, you can think of its decimal and then write the decimal as a fraction using the place value of the decimal number.)

Note: When operating with fractions whose decimal representation is non-terminating, using fraction form leads to an accurate result, whereas working in decimal form does not. This issue is raised in ACE Exercise 29.

1.4 Decimal Sum and Difference Algorithms

Mathematical Goals

- Develop and use efficient algorithms for adding and subtracting decimals
- Explore the inverse relationship between addition and subtraction in decimal settings

Launch

Remind students of the work they have done with decimals and fractions. Talk with the class about what an algorithm is in mathematics.

- *Can someone explain what an algorithm is?*

Look at the algorithm for adding fractions developed in *Bits and Pieces II*. Once students are comfortable with what an algorithm is, read through the questions in Problem 1.4. Have students work individually on Question A, then work in pairs or small groups to discuss their algorithms.

Explore

Have students record their final algorithms on transparency film or chart paper to share with the class. As students work with fact families and missing-value problems, note whether or not students are focusing on the relationship between addition and subtraction. Do students use the idea that the sum in an addition problem will be the amount from which you subtract (minuend) in a subtraction problem? For $a + b = c$, the related subtraction problems are $c - b = a$ and $c - a = b$.

Materials
- Chart paper, or blank transparency film
- Marker (optional)

Summarize

Have students share their algorithms for adding and subtracting fractions. It is helpful to have students demonstrate how their algorithm works on a problem. With both fraction and decimal place-value approaches, have students talk about why their algorithm works.

- *Why do we need to line up the decimal points?*
- *Can someone describe what the decimal approach and the fraction approach have in common?*
- *Let's try this algorithm on this problem. Does it account for all the things you have to think about to solve this problem?*

The class does not have to develop only one algorithm, but students should have an algorithm that they can explain and use.

With Question C, focus on the strategies students used to determine the value of N. Look for opportunities to discuss how a fact family can be helpful.

Materials
- Student notebooks

continued on next page

Question D asks students to work a problem that combines fractions and decimals. One possibility is to rewrite $2\frac{1}{8}$ as a decimal, making the problem $4.27 - 2.125$. Another possibility is to rewrite 4.27 as a fraction, $4\frac{27}{100}$. Then you need to rename $2\frac{1}{8}$ as a fraction with a power of ten in the denominator.

ACE Assignment Guide for Problem 1.4

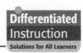

Core 23–32, 45, 46

Other *Applications* 33–36, *Extensions* 53–58; unassigned choices from previous exercises

Adapted For suggestions about adapting ACE exercises, see the CMP *Special Needs Handbook*.
Connecting to Prior Units 45, 46: *Shapes and Designs*

Answers to Problem 1.4

A. Possible algorithms:

- When adding or subtracting decimals, first line up the decimal points in order to line up the place value of the digits. If the number is a whole number, place the ones place in the appropriate whole number position so the other digits are also in the appropriate place value position. Add or subtract each place value according to the algorithm. Be sure to place the decimal between the ones and tenths place in the answer. This will happen automatically if you place a decimal in the answer so that it is lined up with the decimals in the numbers you are adding or subtracting.

- Change the decimals to fractions with a power of ten in the denominator. Next, add or subtract the fractions, using common denominators if needed. Rename the fraction answer as a decimal number.

B. 1. $0.02 + 0.103 = 0.123$;
$0.103 + 0.02 = 0.123$;
$0.123 - 0.02 = 0.103$; and
$0.123 - 0.103 = 0.02$

2. $1.82 - 0.103 = 1.717; 1.82 - 1.717 = 0.103$;
$1.717 + 0.103 = 1.82$; and
$0.103 + 1.717 = 1.82$

C. 1. $N = 84.275$

2. $N = 40.3$

3. $N = 4.25$

4. $N = 14.09$

D. 1. $4.27 - 2.125 = 2.145$

2. $4\frac{27}{100} - 2\frac{125}{1,000} = 4\frac{270}{1,000} - 2\frac{125}{1,000} = 2\frac{145}{1,000}$ or 2.145

Investigation 1

Decimals—More or Less!

In this unit you will consider everyday situations in which decimals are used. For example, you can measure a person's height using inches or centimeters, and then record the results as a decimal. So, 66 inches is 5.5 feet, and 102 cm is 1.02 meters. You can measure the time it takes a person to run a race, and then record the results. You can also use decimals to find the cost of items that you buy at the store.

1.1 About How Much?

When you are working with decimals, it is helpful to use what you know about fractions. Here is a number line labeled with some of the fraction and decimal benchmarks you learned about in *Bits and Pieces I*.

0	$\frac{1}{4}$	$\frac{1}{2}$	$\frac{3}{4}$	1	$1\frac{1}{4}$	$1\frac{1}{2}$	$1\frac{3}{4}$	2
0	0.25	0.5	0.75	1	1.25	1.5	1.75	2

These benchmarks are useful when you are estimating with decimals. For example, you can use a benchmark to quickly estimate the total amount of a bill.

Notes _____

_____

_____

_____

Tat Ming estimates total cost as he adds items to his cart in the grocery store. He wants to make sure he has enough money to pay the cashier. He puts the following items in his cart:

Chips	$2.79	Salsa	$1.99	Ground Beef	$3.12
Cheese	$1.29	Jalapeños	$0.45		

- Estimate the total cost and tell what you think he might be making for his friends!

- Tat Ming has only $10.00. From your estimate, does he have enough money? How confident are you of your answer?

As you work with decimals in this unit, estimate before you start the calculations. This will help you to know what answer to expect. If your estimate and your answer are not close, you may have made a mistake in calculating, even if you are using a calculator.

Problem **1.1** Estimating With Decimals

For each situation decide which operation to use. Then use benchmarks and other strategies to estimate the sum or difference.

A. Nick is going to Big Thrifty Acres to spend the $20 he got for a birthday present. His mom offers to pay the sales tax for him. He cannot spend more than $20. As he walks through the store, he has to estimate the total cost of all the items he wants to buy.

1. Nick chooses a game that costs $6.89. About how much money will be left if he buys the game?

6 Bits and Pieces III

Notes _____

2. Nick finds some other things he would like to have. He finds a CD on sale for $5.99, a package of basketball cards for $2.89, a bag of peanuts for $1.59, and a baseball hat for $4.29. Does Nick have enough money to buy everything he wants?

3. In this situation, would you overestimate or underestimate? Why?

4. Nick decides to spend $10 and save the rest for another time. What can Nick buy from the items he wants to come as close as possible to spending $10?

B. Maria is saving to buy a new bicycle. The price for the bike she wants is $129.89. She has saved $78 from babysitting. She owes her brother $5. Her grandmother gives her $25 for her birthday. She expects another $10 or $12 from babysitting this weekend. She empties her piggy bank and finds $13.73. Should she plan to buy the bike next week? Why or why not?

C. What strategies do you find useful in estimating sums and differences with decimals?

ACE **Homework starts on page 13.**

STUDENT PAGE

Notes _____

_____

_____

_____

Perhaps something like the following happened to you.

Getting Ready for **Problem** **1.2**

Sally Jane and her friend Zeke buy snacks at Quick Shop. They pick out a bag of pretzels for $0.89 and a half-gallon of cider for $1.97. The cash register in the express lane is broken and the clerk says the bill (before taxes) is $10.87.

- Do you agree? If not, explain what the clerk probably did wrong.

It looks like the Quick Shop clerk does not know about place value! For example, in the numbers 236.5 and 23.65, the 2, 3, 6, and 5 mean different things because the decimal point is in a different place. The chart below shows the two numbers and the place value for each digit.

- Why is it an error for the clerk to add the 8 in the price of the pretzels to the 1 in the price of the cider?

Here is a situation that uses decimals but does not involve money. Use what you know about measurement and place value to help you think about the problems.

Every year, students at Memorial High School volunteer to clean local highway roadsides. Each club or team at the school is assigned a section of highway to clean.

One member of a club measures out each member's part of the section of highway using a trundle wheel. A trundle wheel can measure distances in thousandths of a mile.

8   Bits and Pieces III

Notes _____

_____

_____

_____

A. Solve each problem. Write a mathematical sentence using decimal notation to show your computation. Record your sentence in a table like the one below. You will add to your table in Problem 1.3.

Person	Number Sentence (decimal notation)	(Leave this column blank for Problem 1.3)
Carmela		

1. Carmela signed up to clean 1.5 miles for the cross-country team. It starts to rain after she has cleaned 0.25 of a mile. How much does she have left to clean?

2. Pam cleans 0.25 of a mile for the chorus and cleans another 0.375 of a mile for the math club. How much does she clean altogether?

3. Jim, a member of the chess club, first cleans 0.287 of a mile. He later cleans another 0.02 of a mile. How much of a mile does he clean altogether?

4. Teri doesn't notice that she finished her section of highway until she is 0.005 of a mile past her goal of 0.85 of a mile. She claims she cleaned nine tenths of a mile. Is she correct? Explain.

B. 1. Explain what place value has to do with adding and subtracting decimals.

2. Use your ideas about place value and adding and subtracting decimals to solve the following problems.

a. $27.9 + 103.2$ **b.** $0.45 + 1.2$

c. $2.011 + 1.99$ **d.** $34.023 - 1.23$

e. $4.32 - 1.746$ **f.** $0.982 - 0.2$

ACE Homework starts on page 13.

Notes _____

_____

_____

_____

STUDENT PAGE (right margin)

Using Fractions to Add and Subtract Decimals

To add or subtract decimals, you have to be sure to only add or subtract digits that have the same place value. You can make sure by writing addition and subtraction problems in column form and lining up the decimal points.

You can use your knowledge of fractions to see why this strategy for adding or subtracting decimals works. Remember that decimals can be written as fractions with 10; 100; 1,000; 10,000; etc. as denominators. Revisit the Quick Shop problem and think of the money amounts as fractions.

Getting Ready for **Problem**

Remember that Sally Jane and her friend Zeke went to Quick Shop to buy snacks. They picked out a bag of pretzels for $0.89 and a half-gallon of cider for $1.97.

$$0.89 = \frac{89}{100}$$

$$1.97 = \frac{197}{100}$$

So the total cost is $\frac{89}{100} + \frac{197}{100} = \frac{286}{100} = 2.86$.

How is this like thinking of the cost in pennies and then finally writing the sum in dollars?

Problem 1.3 **Using Fractions to Add and Subtract Decimals**

A. Write the decimal numbers in parts (1)–(4) in fraction form with denominators of 10, 100, 1000, etc. Then add or subtract the fractions. Write a number sentence in fraction notation that shows your computation. Add it to your table in Problem 1.2.

1. Carmela signed up to clean 1.5 miles for the cross-country team. It starts to rain after she has cleaned 0.25 of a mile. How much does she have left to clean?

2. Pam cleans 0.25 of a mile for the chorus and cleans another 0.375 of a mile for the math club. How much does she clean altogether?

10   Bits and Pieces III

Notes _____

_____

_____

_____

3. Jim, a member of the chess club, first cleans 0.287 of a mile. He later cleans another 0.02 of a mile. How much of a mile does he clean altogether?

4. Teri doesn't notice that she finished her section of highway until she is 0.005 of a mile past her goal of 0.85 of a mile. She claims she cleaned nine tenths of a mile. Is she correct? Explain.

B. Use your table to compare your sentences in Problem 1.3A to those you wrote in Problem 1.2A. How does the fraction method help explain why you can line up the decimals and add digits with the same place values to find the answer?

C. Fraction benchmarks are a useful way to estimate in decimal situations. For parts (1)–(6), write a number sentence using fraction benchmarks to estimate the sum or difference.

1. $1.199 + 2.02$ **2.** $1.762 + 6.9$ **3.** $0.243 + 0.7$

4. $3.724 - 0.49$ **5.** $6.899 - 2.9$ **6.** $7.5097 - 1.008$

ACE Homework starts on page 13.

Notes _____

_____

_____

_____

1.4 Decimal Sum and Difference Algorithms

You have looked at how place value and fraction addition and subtraction can help you make sense of adding and subtracting decimals. You can use those ideas to describe an algorithm for adding and subtracting decimals.

Problem 1.4 Decimal Sum and Difference Algorithms

A. Use your experiences adding and subtracting decimals in money and measurement situations. Describe an algorithm for adding and subtracting decimal numbers.

B. In *Bits and Pieces II*, you learned about fact families. Here is an addition-subtraction fact family that uses fractions:

$$\frac{1}{2} + \frac{1}{3} = \frac{5}{6} \qquad \frac{1}{3} + \frac{1}{2} = \frac{5}{6} \qquad \frac{5}{6} - \frac{1}{2} = \frac{1}{3} \qquad \frac{5}{6} - \frac{1}{3} = \frac{1}{2}$$

1. Write the complete addition-subtraction fact family for
0.02 + 0.103 = 0.123.

2. Write the complete addition-subtraction fact family for
1.82 − 0.103 = 1.717.

C. Find the value of N that makes the mathematical sentence correct. Fact families might help.

1. 63.2 + 21.075 = N

2. 44.32 − 4.02 = N

3. N + 2.3 = 6.55

4. N − 6.88 = 7.21

D. 1. Explain how you can solve the problem $4.27 - 2\frac{1}{8}$ by changing $2\frac{1}{8}$ to a decimal.

2. Explain how you can solve the problem $4.27 - 2\frac{1}{8}$ by changing 4.27 to a fraction.

ACE Homework starts on page 13.

Notes _____

_____

_____

_____

Applications

For Exercises 1–6, tell whether the number is closest to 0, $\frac{1}{2}$, or 1. Explain your reasoning.

1. 0.07
2. 1.150
3. 0.391

4. 0.0999
5. 0.99
6. 0.599

7. Billie goes to the fabric store to buy material and other items she needs for a project. She has $16.95 to spend. The material costs $8.69. A container of craft glue costs $1.95. A package of craft paper is $4.29.

  a. Estimate how much it will cost to buy the material, glue, and craft paper.

  b. Did you overestimate or underestimate? Explain.

  c. Billie also finds a package of ribbon that costs $2.89. Based on your estimate in part (a), how much more money does she need if she buys the ribbon? Explain.

Add or subtract.

8. 3.42 + 5.8
9. 5.012 + 0.93
10. 10.437 + 4.0034

11. 0.403 + 0.07
12. 5.2 − 0.12
13. 4.54 − 2.9

14. 0.095 − 0.0071
15. 2.057 − 1.99
16. 10.91 − 1.068

Go Online
PHSchool.com
For: Multiple-Choice Skills Practice
Web Code: ama-6154

17. Ms. Palkowski cleans 0.125 of a mile of highway for a group of teachers and then 0.4 of a mile for the science club. How much does she clean altogether?

18. Multiple Choice Which is correct?

A.
$$\begin{array}{r} 81.9 \\ +\ \underline{0.62} \\ 88.1 \end{array}$$

B.
$$\begin{array}{r} 81.9 \\ +\ \underline{0.62} \\ 82.52 \end{array}$$

C.
$$\begin{array}{r} 81.9 \\ +\ \underline{0.62} \\ 8.81 \end{array}$$

D.
$$\begin{array}{r} 81.9 \\ +\ \underline{0.62} \\ 0.881 \end{array}$$

Investigation 1 Decimals—More or Less! **13**

Notes _____

_____

_____

_____

19. Estimate using fraction benchmarks.

    a. 2.43 + 1.892   **b.** 4.694 − 1.23   **c.** 12.92 + 3.506 − 6.18

20. Gregory walks 1.8 miles from his home to school. Halfway between his home and school there is a music store. This morning, he wants to stop at the store before school. Right now he is 0.36 miles away from home.

    a. How much more does he need to walk, in miles, to get to the store?

    b. How many miles does he have left to walk to school?

21. Christopher, Tim, Lee, and Dwayne are running in a 4 × 100-meter relay race. Christopher runs his stretch in 12.35 seconds, Tim takes 13.12 seconds, and Lee takes 11.91. If the team wants to break the school record of 48.92 seconds, how fast will Dwayne have to run?

22. Karen, Lou, and Jeff each bought a miniature tree. They measured the height of their trees once a month over the five months from December to April.

Miniature Tree Height (m)					
	December	**January**	**February**	**March**	**April**
Karen's Tree	0.794	0.932	1.043	1.356	1.602
Lou's Tree	0.510	0.678	0.84	1.34	1.551
Jeff's Tree	0.788	0.903	1.22	1.452	1.61

a. Who had the tallest tree at the beginning?

b. Whose tree was the tallest at the end of April?

c. Whose tree grew fastest during the first month?

d. Whose tree grew by the most from December to April?

14   Bits and Pieces III

Notes _____

_____

_____

_____

Add or subtract.

23. $\frac{4}{5} + \frac{3}{4}$ **24.** $2\frac{3}{5} + \frac{3}{8}$ **25.** $1\frac{2}{3} + 3\frac{5}{6}$

26. $\frac{8}{3} - \frac{4}{5}$ **27.** $1\frac{4}{5} - \frac{1}{2}$ **28.** $4\frac{2}{8} - 1\frac{3}{4}$

29. Rewrite Exercises 23–28 with decimal numbers and find the results of the operations using the decimal equivalents of the numbers. Compare your decimal answers to the fraction answers.

30. Solve. Then write the complete addition-subtraction fact family.

    a. $22.3 + 31.65 = N$ **b.** $18.7 - 4.24 = N$

31. Add.

    a. $4.9 + 3\frac{3}{4}$ **b.** $91.678 + 2.34 + 12.001$ **c.** $2.75 + 3\frac{2}{5}$

32. Find the value of N that makes the mathematical sentence correct. Use fact families to help you.

    a. $2.3 + N = 3.42$ **b.** $N - 11.6 = 3.75$

33. Find the missing numbers.

    a.   36.03   **b.**
         + ▬▬▬▬   + 0.488
           45.218   13.762

    c. $0.45 + N + 0.4 = 2.62$ **d.** $75.4 - 10.801 + N = 77.781$

34. Place decimal points in 102 and 19 so that the sum of the two numbers is 1.21.

35. Place decimal points in 34, 4, and 417 so that the sum of the three numbers is 7.97.

36. Place decimal points in 431 and 205 so that the difference between the two numbers is 16.19.

Notes _____

_____

_____

_____

Connections

37. Which of the numbers is the greatest? How do you know?

     81.9   81.90   81.900

Homework Help Online
PHSchool.com
For: Help with Exercise 37
Web Code: ame-6137

38. **Multiple Choice** Which group of decimals is ordered from least to greatest?

   A. 5.6, 5.9, 5.09, 5.96, 5.139

   B. 0.112, 1.012, 1.3, 1.0099, 10.12

   C. 2.8, 2.109, 2.72, 2.1, 2.719

   D. 0.132, 0.23, 0.383, 0.3905, 0.392

39. Find the missing lengths. Then find the perimeter of the figure.
   (All units are in inches.)

For Exercises 40–43, name the geometric figures and find their perimeters.
(All units are in inches. The figures are not drawn to scale.)

40.

41.

STUDENT PAGE

Notes _____

_____

_____

_____

42.

43.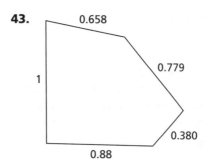

44. The perimeter of a parallelogram is 15.42 cm. The length of one of its sides is 2.93 cm. What are the lengths of its other sides?

Find the measures of the missing angles.

45.

46.

Extensions

47. a. In order to add 3 dollars and 35 cents to 5 dollars and 78 cents, you can write each amount as a decimal. Since 3.35 + 5.78 = 9.13, the total is 9 dollars and 13 cents.

Now consider adding time values in a similar way. For example, can you add 2 hours and 45 minutes to 3 hours and 57 minutes by using decimal numbers (2.45 + 3.57)? Explain.

b. Consider length measurements. You can add 13 meters and 47 centimeters to 4 meters and 72 centimeters using decimal numbers. Since 13.47 + 4.72 = 18.19, the total length is 18 meters and 19 centimeters.

Suppose you want to add 3 feet and 7 inches to 5 feet 6 inches. Can you apply the same idea so that you add 3.7 to 5.6 to get the total length? Explain.

Notes _____
_____
_____
_____

48. Mark says that 3.002 must be smaller than 3.0019 since 2 is smaller than 19. How can you convince him that he is wrong?

For Exercises 49–52, use 1, 2, 3, or 4 to form decimal numbers so that each sum or difference is as close as possible to the given number. You may use the same digit twice in one number. For example, you may write 0.33. The symbol ≈ means "is approximately equal to."

49. $0.\blacksquare\blacksquare + 0.\blacksquare\blacksquare \approx \frac{1}{3}$

50. $0.\blacksquare\blacksquare - 0.\blacksquare\blacksquare \approx 0.125$

51. $0.\blacksquare\blacksquare - 0.\blacksquare\blacksquare \approx \frac{2}{7}$

52. $0.\blacksquare\blacksquare + 0.\blacksquare\blacksquare \approx 0.9$

For Exercises 53 and 54, use 1, 2, 3, or 4 to form decimal numbers so that each calculation is correct. You may use the same digit twice in one number.

53. $0.\blacksquare\blacksquare + 0.\blacksquare\blacksquare = 0.75$

54. $0.\blacksquare\blacksquare - 0.\blacksquare\blacksquare = 0.3$

55. Use the numbers 2, 9, 7, and 4 only once in each part to complete each decimal.

   a. Write the greatest possible number of the form 3.$\blacksquare\blacksquare\blacksquare\blacksquare$.

   b. Write the least possible number of the form 3.$\blacksquare\blacksquare\blacksquare\blacksquare$.

   c. Write all the possible numbers of the form 3.$\blacksquare\blacksquare\blacksquare\blacksquare$ that are greater than 3.795.

   d. Write all the possible numbers of the form 3.$\blacksquare\blacksquare\blacksquare\blacksquare$ that are less than 3.73 but greater than 3.4399.

56. Use the fact that there are 16 ounces in a pound to answer parts (a)–(d).

   a. How many pounds are in 256 ounces?

   b. How many ounces are in 0.125 pound?

   c. How many ounces are in 3.375 pounds?

   d. How many pounds are in 17 ounces? Express this as a mixed number and as a decimal.

Notes _____

_____

_____

_____

57. Julie has a bread recipe that calls for 1.75 pounds of flour.

   a. She wants to make this recipe three times. How much flour does she need?

   b. She has no flour at home. How many 5-pound bags of flour should she buy to make the recipe three times?

   c. A ton is 2,000 pounds. Estimate how many loaves of bread she could make with a ton of flour.

58. Will likes to keep track of his friends on road clean-up day. He thinks of himself as being at 0 on the number line below. Friends who are on the road ahead of him he pictures to the right on a number line. Friends who are on the road behind him he pictures to the left.

Sample Tamika is 3 km ahead, at +3. Cyrus is 2 km behind, at −2. We read "+3" as "positive three" and "−2" as "negative 2."

   a. Justin is 3 km behind Will. Mark his position on a copy of the number line above.

   b. Carlos is at the location shown on the number line. Is Carlos ahead of or behind Will? By how many kilometers?

   c. Write three more numbers that show locations behind Will.

   d. Write three numbers that show locations ahead of Will.

Investigation 1 Decimals—More or Less!   **19**

Notes _____

_____

_____

_____

Mathematical Reflections 1

In this investigation you looked at situations involving measurement data and money written as decimals. You found strategies for estimating addition or subtraction involving decimals. You used your understanding of fractions and place value to develop algorithms for adding and subtracting decimals. The following questions will help you summarize what you have learned.

Think about your answers to these questions. Discuss your ideas with other students and your teacher. Then write a summary of your findings in your notebook.

1. Describe one strategy that you found helpful in estimating sums or differences of decimals. Explain why it was helpful to you.

2. How does interpreting decimals as fractions help you make sense of adding and subtracting decimals? Use an example to help show your thinking.

3. How does the place value interpretation of decimals help you add and subtract decimals? Use an example to help show your thinking.

4. Describe an algorithm for adding and subtracting any two decimal numbers.

Notes

Answers

Investigation ①

ACE Assignment Choices

Differentiated Instruction
Solutions for All Learners

Problem 1.1
Core 1–6; 37–38
Other *Applications* 7

Problem 1.2
Core 8–18
Other *Connections* 39; *Extensions* 47, 48;
unassigned choices from previous problems

Problem 1.3
Core 19–21
Other *Applications* 22, *Connections* 40–44,
Extensions 49–52; unassigned choices from
previous problems

Problem 1.4
Core 23–32, 45, 46
Other *Applications* 33–36, *Extensions* 53–58;
unassigned choices from previous problems

Adapted For suggestions about adapting Exercise
20 and other ACE exercises, see the CMP *Special
Needs Handbook*.
Connecting to Prior Units 37–38: *Bits and Pieces I;*
39–44: *Covering and Surrounding;* 40–43, 45, 46:
Shapes and Designs

Applications

1. Close to 0 since 0.07 is less than 0.1.

2. Close to 1 since it is already greater than 1.

3. Close to $\frac{1}{2}$ since the midpoint between 0 and $\frac{1}{2}$
   is 0.25 and 0.391 is greater than 0.25.

4. Close to 0 since 0.0999 is less than 0.1.

5. Close to 1 since it is only 0.01 away from 1.

6. Close to $\frac{1}{2}$ since the midpoint between $\frac{1}{2}$ and 1
   is 0.75 and 0.599 is less than 0.75.

7. **a.** Possible answer: about $15.25;
   $8.75 + 2 + 4.25 = \$15$.

b. This is an overestimate since two numbers
are rounded to a number greater than their
value. Overestimation makes more sense
because if Billie has enough money to
cover the overestimation that means
she can cover the actual amount. An
underestimation may be misleading since
the actual amount will be greater than
this value and being able to cover the
underestimation does not always mean that
one has enough money for the actual
amount.

c. She needs about $1. After material, glue,
and paper, she will have about $1.95 left.
The ribbon is about $3. So, the difference
gives $1.

8. 9.22

9. 5.942

10. 14.4404

11. 0.473

12. 5.08

13. 1.64

14. 0.0879

15. 0.067

16. 9.842

17. 0.525 mi

18. B

19. **a.** Possible answer: $2\frac{1}{2} + 2 = 4\frac{1}{2}$
    b. Possible answer: $4\frac{3}{4} - 1\frac{1}{4} = 3\frac{1}{2}$
    c. Possible answer: $13 + 3\frac{1}{2} - 6 = 10\frac{1}{2}$

20. **a.** 0.54 mi   **b.** 1.44 mi

21. 11.54 seconds. Possible answer:
    $48.92 - 12.35 - 13.12 - 11.91 = 11.54$ seconds

22. **a.** Karen
    b. Jeff's tree
    c. Lou's tree; it grew 0.168 meters from
    December to January.
    d. Lou's tree; it grew 1.041 meters from
    December to April.

23. $1\frac{11}{20}$

24. $2\frac{39}{40}$

25. $5\frac{1}{2}$

26. $1\frac{13}{15}$

27. $1\frac{3}{10}$

28. $2\frac{1}{2}$

29. a. $0.8 + 0.75 = 1.55$

    b. $2.6 + 0.375 = 2.975$

    c. Using decimal approximation of 2 decimal places for non-terminating decimals: $1.67 + 3.83 = 5.50$. (Note that the decimal solution may not be equivalent to the fraction solution. If students had used $1.6 + 3.8$ their sum would not be 5.5. Briefly talk with students about why this happens with non-terminating decimals.)

    d. Using decimal approximation of 2 decimal places for non-terminating decimals: $2.67 - 0.8 = 1.87$. (Note that the decimal solution may not be equivalent to the fraction solution. Briefly talk with students about why this happens with non-terminating decimals.)

    e. $1.8 - 0.5 = 1.3$

    f. $4.25 - 1.75 = 2.5$

30. a. N = 53.95; $22.3 + 31.65 = 53.95$; $31.65 + 22.3 = 53.95$; $53.95 - 22.3 = 31.65$; and $53.95 - 31.65 = 22.3$

    b. N = 14.46; $18.7 - 4.24 = 14.46$; $18.7 - 14.46 = 4.24$; $14.46 + 4.24 = 18.7$; and $4.24 + 14.46 = 18.7$

31. a. 8.65

    b. 106.019

    c. 6.15

32. a. N = 1.12

    b. N = 15.35

33. a. missing number is 9.188

    b. missing number is 13.274

    c. missing number is 1.77

    d. missing number is 13.182

34. $1.02 + 0.19 = 1.21$

35. $3.4 + 4.17 + 0.4 = 7.97$

36. $20.5 - 4.31 = 16.19$

Connections

37. All three numbers are equivalent. All have 81 wholes, 9 tenths and no value or zero in all other place value spots.

38. D

39. $a = 1.83$ in., $b = 0.62$ in., $c = 1.82$ in., $d = 2.71$ in., $e = 2.71$ in. Perimeter = 14.92 in.

40. isosceles triangle, perimeter = 1.832 in.

41. trapezoid (assuming that the sides with lengths 8.68 and 3.06 are parallel; quadrilateral is also an acceptable answer); perimeter = 26.63 in.

42. quadrilateral (some students may recognize this as a kite, which is common, but not used in CMP); perimeter = 229.2 in.

43. pentagon; perimeter = 3.697 in.

44. 4.78 cm, 2.93 cm, and 4.78 cm

45. $180 - 28.1 - 53.18 = 98.72°$

46. $180 - 98.72 - 28.1 = 53.18°$

Extensions

47. a. We cannot add 2 hours and 45 minutes to 3 hours and 57 minutes by using $2.45 + 3.57$. This is because 0.45 in the decimal part of 2.45 means 0.45 hours. On the other hand, 45 minutes is 0.75 hours (i.e. $\frac{3}{4}$ of an hour). So, 2 hours and 45 minutes, in decimal form, is equal to 2.75, not 2.45. The idea of writing cents as decimal numbers works for money calculations because one cent written in dollar units is 0.01 dollar. Both the cent and decimal representation of the numbers have the same digits: 35 cents = $0.35 and 78 cents = $0.78.

    b. Similar to part a, we cannot just add 3.7 to 5.6. This is because 7 in. is not 0.7 ft and 6 in. is not 0.6 ft.

48. The digit 2 in 3.002 means 2 thousandths, while 19 in 3.0019 means 19 ten thousandths, or 1.9 thousandths. So, 3.002 must be greater than 3.0019. An easy way to compare these kinds of numbers would be to consider 3.002 as equal to 3.0020 (the extra zero at the end does not change the value of the number) and compare 20 with 19 since both numbers now have the same number of decimal digits.

49–54. Possible answers given.

49. $0.12 + 0.21 \approx \frac{1}{3}$ or $0.22 + 0.11 \approx \frac{1}{3}$

50. $0.24 - 0.12 \approx 0.125$ or $0.23 - 0.11 \approx 0.125$

51. $0.42 - 0.13 \approx \frac{2}{7}$

52. $0.44 + 0.44 \approx 0.9$ (This is the closest one can get to 0.9 under the given restrictions.)

53. $0.32 + 0.43 = 0.75$ or $0.44 + 0.31 = 0.75$

54. $0.41 - 0.11 = 0.3$

55. a. 3.9742

   b. 3.2479

   c. 3.9724, 3.9742, 3.9274, 3.9247, 3.9472, 3.9427

   d. 3.7294, 3.7249, 3.4729, 3.4792, 3.4927, 3.4972

56. a. 16 lb

   b. 2 oz

   c. 54 oz

   d. $1\frac{1}{16}$ or 1.0625 lb

57. a. 5.25 lb

   b. Two bags. She will have lots of flour left over.

   c. About 1,000 loaves.

58. a.

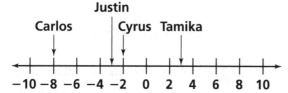

   b. −8. He is 8 kilometers behind Will.

   c. Answers will vary. Any three negative numbers are correct.

   d. Answers will vary. Any three positive numbers are cor.rect.

Possible Answers to Mathematical Reflections

1. There are several possible strategies. Rounding each decimal number to the nearest whole number is often an easy and effective strategy. If a sum involves more than two or three addends, one might take care not to round all of the numbers up (nor to round all of them down) to avoid having a sum that is much too great (or too small). For lesser sums and differences, one might estimate a decimal with a fraction that is easy to work with, then use fraction estimation skills.

2. Thinking of a decimal in terms of fractions allows us to use familiar fraction addition algorithms. To add 0.35 and 0.4, we can write: $\frac{35}{100} + \frac{4}{10} = \frac{35}{100} + \frac{40}{100} = \frac{75}{100}$. Viewed as fractions, we can see that we need to think of 0.4 as 0.40 to have a common denominator to combine with 0.35. Getting a common denominator is like lining up the place values because your numbers have the same size pieces.

3. The place-value interpretation helps to clarify the need for lining up decimal points. It is not just the decimal points that are being lined up, it is all of the place values. We need to add tenths to tenths, hundredths to hundredths, etc. when adding decimals. In the previous example, we need to add the "4" to the "3" in 0.35, not to the "5" because both the "4" and the "3" represent tenths. We would not add four dimes to 5 pennies and say that we have 9 cents.

4. Possible answer:

Place Value Algorithm: When adding or subtracting decimals, first line up the decimal points so it lines up the place value. Add or subtract as you would with whole numbers. Place the decimal between the ones and tenths place in the answer. This will happen automatically if you place a decimal in the answer so that it is lined up with the decimals in the numbers you are adding or subtracting.

Fraction Algorithm: Change the decimal numbers to fractions with powers of ten in the denominator. Next, add or subtract the fractions, using common denominators if needed. Rename the fraction answer as a decimal number.

Investigation 2 Decimal Times

Mathematical and Problem-Solving Goals

- Estimate the relative size of a decimal product prior to finding an exact answer.
- Develop place-value understanding of decimal multiplication
- Solve problems that require decimal multiplication
- Consider how finding a decimal part of and a fraction part of a quantity affects the relative size of a product
- Use place value to reason about decimal multiplication
- Explore the relationship between factors and products in decimal multiplication
- Develop estimation strategies for finding decimal products
- Use estimation as a strategy for locating the position of the decimal in finding exact decimal products
- Generalize an approach to placing the decimal point into a product that involves counting and adding decimal places
- Consider when various strategies are useful for finding decimal products
- Understand what happens to place value and the position of the decimal when you multiply by powers of ten
- Develop at least one efficient algorithm for multiplying decimals

Summary of Problems

Problem 2.1 Relating Fraction and Decimal Multiplication

Students use fractions to help make sense of multiplication of decimals. The students estimate a product, express decimals as fractions, multiply the fractions, write the answer as a decimal, and look for patterns that relate the number of decimal places in the factors to the number of decimal places in the answer.

Problem 2.2 Missing Factors

Problem 2.2 focuses on factors, rather than products, that will produce given decimal products.

Problem 2.3 Finding Decimal Products

Students explore strategies for estimating products and use estimation as a strategy for placing the decimal point into a product.

Problem 2.4 Factor–Product Relationships

Students investigate the relationship between the sum of the number of decimal places in the factors and the number of decimal places in a product. Students explore patterns to investigate the outcome of multiplication by powers of ten on the placement of the decimal point in a product.

Mathematics Background

For background on decimal multiplication, estimation, and computation, see pages 5–6.

	Suggested Pacing	Materials for Students	Materials for Teachers	ACE Assignments
All	6 days			
2.1	$1\frac{1}{2}$ days	Blank transparency film, markers (optional)	Transparency 2.1; Summary Transparency 2.1	1–6, 34–39, 46–48
2.2	1 day			7–16
2.3	1 day		Transparency 2.3	17–24, 40–44, 49
2.4	2 days	Calculators (optional), Labsheet 2.4	Transparency 2.4	25–33, 45, 50–55
MR	$\frac{1}{2}$ day			

Relating Fraction and Decimal Multiplication

Goals

- Estimate the relative size of a decimal product prior to finding an exact answer

- Develop place-value understanding of decimal multiplication

- Solve problems that require decimal multiplication

- Consider how finding a decimal part *of* and a fraction part *of* a quantity affects the relative size of a product

This problem provides an opportunity to review fraction multiplication while developing decimal multiplication. We are helping students to understand the meaning behind multiplication algorithms and the role of place value in this process. By using fraction form to develop decimal multiplication, place value is made explicit. Students should understand finite decimals as fractions with special denominators (powers of 10). So 3.5×0.25 can be thought of as $\frac{35}{10} \times \frac{25}{100}$ (or $3\frac{5}{10} \times \frac{25}{100}$). We are multiplying tenths by hundredths. Students' understanding of fraction multiplication justifies that the answer ought to be in thousandths.

The standard rule for multiplying decimals is that there needs to be as many decimal places in the product as there are in the two factors combined. Thus, the product $3.5 \times 0.25 = 7.175$ has one decimal place in the first factor, two decimal places in the second factor and three $(1 + 2)$ decimal places in the product (7.175). While this rule may surface here, the intention of this problem is to use fraction multiplication to develop place value understanding of decimal multiplication. A place value approach is also the focus in Problems 2.2 and 2.3. The counting and adding decimal places approach will be explored in Problem 2.4 and connected to fraction and place value approaches to understand *why* this works.

Launch 2.1

Use the introductory material regarding place value and decimals to revisit fraction multiplication. Consider how multiplication where quantities are written in decimal form is related to multiplication where quantities are written in fraction form. While the problem uses a base-ten area model, it may be useful to relate this to the brownie pan area model used to develop fraction multiplication in *Bits and Pieces II*.

Briefly review the connection between place value in decimals and the denominator of the fraction form of the same number. Reintroduce the idea of writing decimal computation problems in fraction form and work through the Getting Ready with the class. Be sure to estimate the product to decide if the product is reasonable.

Suggested Questions One way to launch the problem is to have a conversation with your students about naming amounts with fractions. Pose questions like the following:

- *What would be a reasonable estimate for 0.3×2.3, or $\frac{3}{10} \times 2\frac{3}{10}$?* (The product will be about 1 since 0.3 is a little less than $\frac{1}{2}$ and 2.3 is a little more than 2, and $\frac{1}{2}$ of 2 is 1.)

- *What is the actual product in fraction notation?* $(\frac{69}{100})$

- *What is the product when written as a decimal?* (0.69)

- *How does knowing the product as a fraction help you write the product in decimal form?* (The denominator of the fraction tells us the place value of the numerator. For instance, in the example above, the 100 in the denominator told us that there should be two decimal places in the answer so that the last digit of the numerator would be in the hundredths place.)

You may have some students who already know the rule to count the total number of decimal places. If the issue is raised, ask them to explain why this works. Look to see if they can link the role of place value to this rule, possibly using fraction form to help.

Introduce Problem 2.1 and the Apple-A-Day roadside fruit stand. With Question A, be sure students understand that there are four things they need to do for each part. First, they should estimate each product, then write the decimals as fractions, use fraction multiplication to find the product, and then change each answer to a decimal. Use the estimate as a check.

Have students work in pairs or small groups.

Explore 2.1

As students work, encourage them to formulate rules for decimal multiplication and to connect those rules to their knowledge of fraction multiplication.

Suggested Questions Check to see that students start with an estimate.

- *What did your group decide upon for a reasonable estimate?*

- *How do you know your estimate is reasonable?*

- *Is your estimate greater or less than the actual product? How do you know?*

Students may struggle with decimal multiplication estimation. Suggest the use of benchmark fractions. If students are struggling, you may want to stop and summarize Question A. Discuss estimation in the context of the fruit stand problem, and then have students finish Questions B and C as homework. Be sure to discuss Questions B and C the next day.

Look for students who need help in reviewing fraction multiplication and how to write a decimal as a fraction. Watch for students who write the decimals in fraction form, but the denominator is not a power of 10. For example, with Question A (4), some may write $1\frac{1}{2} \times 1\frac{1}{2}$ rather than $1\frac{5}{10} \times 1\frac{5}{10}$. You may choose to redirect the students or wait until the summary and let the students as a class decide. This idea is also the focus of a summary transparency.

Also look for students who have ideas that should surface in the summary. As students

complete Question A, you may want to have students put their solutions on transparency film or the board to use in the summary.

Summarize 2.1

Start by asking a student to talk about their estimate. Focus on the reasoning that led to the estimate. If students really struggle, you may need to model how to estimate in multiplication situations.

Suggested Question

- *How did you decide that $0.75 was a reasonable estimate for Question A part (1)?* (1.7 is about 1.5 pounds and it is 50 cents a pound or $\frac{1}{2}$ of 1.5.)

Focus on how students use the fraction product to write a decimal product. For example, with Question A part (2), ask:

- *After you multiplied $\frac{4}{10} \times \frac{55}{100}$ to get $\frac{220}{1,000}$, how did you change your fraction to a decimal?* (The denominator is 1,000 so I knew I needed 3 decimal places in my answer. I also know the product is less than 1 so the form of the answer is 0.▪▪▪. I thought 0.▪▪▪ and then placed in my 220 so it had the right number of decimal places and said 220 thousandths, like the fraction.)

- *How are the decimal form and the fraction form the same?* (They both use the product 4×55. In both problems, decimal and fraction form, you use whole number multiplication and then adjust the answer by finding the denominator or by deciding on the placement of the decimal.)

- *How do you decide where to put your decimal in the product?* (The place value or the fraction denominator of the product helps you decide. For example, if your denominator is tenths, put the decimal into the product you found when you multiplied the numerators in the tenths place.)

The goal of Question A is to introduce the use of fraction multiplication as a way to find decimal products. One problem that may surface here, or in later problems is the representations of decimals as fractions that are not powers of 10. A summary transparency is provided to address this issue.

Summary Transparency

For the problem 0.32×0.8 Brandon wrote the following:

$$\frac{32}{100} \times \frac{4}{5} = \frac{128}{500}$$

1. *Now Brandon is stuck! He is not sure how to write this as a decimal. What should he do?* (He could rename $\frac{128}{500}$ as $\frac{256}{1,000}$ and then write the decimal 0.256.)

2. *Why doesn't Brandon's problem have a power of ten in the denominator?* (If he rewrites $\frac{4}{5}$ as $\frac{8}{10}$, he will have a power of 10 in the denominator. Each factor needs a power of 10 in the denominator to assure a power of 10 in the denominator of the product. When the 10 is multiplied by the 100 in $\frac{32}{100}$, the denominator in the product will be 1,000.)

Going Further

- *Can you find two fractions that do not have powers of 10 in the denominator but whose product does have a power of 10 in the denominator? Explain.* (You also can get a power of 10 by having denominators that have only 2's and 5's as factors in equal numbers, i.e., $\frac{4}{2} \times \frac{3}{5}$ or $\frac{4}{2 \cdot 2} \times \frac{3}{5 \cdot 5}$.)

Use Question B to focus on the effect of the size of the factors on each other and the resulting product. An awareness of this effect is important when estimating and determining if a product is reasonable. Students explored this same idea with fraction multiplication. Have students share their examples. You might also find it useful to refer to the problems in Question A.

As you discuss Question B, be attentive to how students are using the context and the numbers. Using A (1) as an example, one might reason that you need to use the $0.50 1.7 times. This is a repeated addition approach. In A (2), the "of" interpretation or $\frac{4}{10}$ *of* $0.55 makes more sense. This is a "part of a part" approach.

Also be attentive to the way students write their multiplication problems. Since multiplication is commutative, one student may write A (1) as 1.7×0.50 while another may write 0.50×1.7. This will affect which problems they use as examples and why.

Suggested Questions After students share their reasoning about Question C, ask:

- *Does multiplication always give an answer greater than the factors?* (Sometimes it does. For example, if you multiply 1.7×2.3, the factor 1.7 indicates that you have 2.3 once and then seven-tenths of 2.3. Multiplying by a number less than 1 leads to taking a part of some quantity. For example, in A (2), 0.4 of a pound is not a whole pound so the cost will be less than, or part of, the cost of a whole pound.)

- *Describe how you can tell whether or not the product will be less than the factor or greater than the factor.*

2.1 Relating Fraction and Decimal Multiplication

Mathematical Goals

- Estimate the relative size of a decimal product prior to finding an exact answer
- Develop place-value understanding of decimal multiplication
- Solve problems that require decimal multiplication
- Consider how finding a decimal part of and a fraction part of a quantity affects the relative size of a product

Launch

Reintroduce the idea of writing decimal computation problems in fraction form and work through the Getting Ready with the class.

- *What would be a reasonable estimate for 0.3 × 2.3, or $\frac{3}{10} \times 2\frac{3}{10}$?*
- *What is the actual product in fraction notation?*
- *What is the product when written as a decimal?*
- *How can knowing the product as a fraction help you write the product in decimal form?*

Introduce Problem 2.1. Be sure students understand there are four things they need to do for each part in Question A. Have students work in pairs or small groups.

Materials

- Transparency 2.1

Explore

Check to see that students start with an estimate.

- *What did your group decide upon for a reasonable estimate?*
- *How do you know your estimate is reasonable?*
- *Is your estimate greater or less than the actual product? How do you know?*

You may want to have students put their solutions on transparency film or the board to use in the summary.

Summarize

Start by discussing estimates. Focus on the reasoning that led to an estimate.

- *How did you decide that $0.75 was a reasonable estimate for Question A part (1)?*

Focus on how students use fraction products to write decimal products. For example, with Question A part (2), ask:

- *After you multiplied $\frac{4}{10} \times \frac{55}{100}$ to get $\frac{220}{1,000}$, how did you change your fraction to a decimal?*

Materials

- Student notebooks
- Summary Transparency 2.1

continued on next page

Summarize

continued

- *How are the decimal form and the fraction form the same?*
- *How do you decide where to put your decimal in the product?*

A summary transparency and a Going Further are provided to raise the issue of representing decimals as fractions that are not powers of 10.

- *Can you find two fractions that do not have powers of 10 in the denominator but whose product does have a power of 10 in the denominator?*

Use Question B to focus on the effect of the size of the factor and factor on each other. Students explored this same idea with fraction multiplication. After students share their reasoning about B1 and B2, ask:

- *Does multiplication always give an answer greater than the factors?*
- *Describe the thinking that would tell you that the product in A1 will be less than the factors.*

Close by talking about question C.

Assignment Guide for Problem 2.1

Core 1–3, 34–39
Other *Applications* 4–6; *Extensions* 46–48

Adapted For suggestions about ACE exercises, see the CMP *Special Needs Handbook*.
Connecting to Prior Units 34–39: *Bits and Pieces II*

Answers to Problem 2.1

A. 1. Possible estimate: $0.75; \frac{17}{10} \times \frac{50}{100} = \frac{850}{1,000}$, or \$0.85

2. Possible estimate: $0.25; \frac{4}{10} \times \frac{55}{100} = \frac{220}{1,000}$, or \$0.22

3. Possible estimate: $3.25; \frac{32}{10} \times \frac{110}{100} = \frac{3,520}{1,000}$, or \$3.52

4. Possible estimate: Since $1\frac{1}{2}$ of 2 is 3, and this is $1\frac{1}{2}$ of $1\frac{1}{2}$, the product will be less than 3, about $2\frac{1}{2}$. (Note that because of the numbers, students may find it just as easy to mentally compute the exact product of 2.25. This is fine if they can explain their reasoning sensibly.) $1\frac{5}{10} \times 1\frac{5}{10}$ or $\frac{15}{10} \times \frac{15}{10} = \frac{225}{100}$, or 2.25 square feet.

B. Possible explanation: You are repeatedly adding a value or taking a part of a part.

C. 1. greater than

Possible example: Question A part (1): $0.50 \times 1.7 = 0.85$; Since the factor 1.7 is greater than 1, you have 1 group of 0.50 and $\frac{7}{10}$ of another group of 0.50. The product will be greater than the other factor 0.50.

2. less than

Possible example: Question A part (1): $1.7 \times 0.50 = 0.85$; since the factor 0.50 is less than 1, or $\frac{1}{2}$, the product will be $\frac{1}{2}$ of 1.7 or less than the factor 1.7.

Goals

- Use place value to reason about decimal multiplication

- Explore the relationship between factors and products in decimal multiplication

In the previous problem, students found products that involved decimals. They will now find factors that will produce a given product. Continue to use fraction multiplication and place value to make sense of the relationship between the factors and the product.

Focus on the meaning behind the fraction form of decimal multiplication. You may find that for some students the reasoning can be done without writing out the problem in fraction form. For example, with 0.5×0.5 students may be able to reason that the whole number problem is $5 \times 5 = 25$. The factors are each tenths, so the product will be hundredths or 0.25.

Keep in mind, though, that many students need to see this reasoning notated. By modeling what is happening with place value using fraction form, you help students understand the place value of products, which is implied in decimal notation.

Launch 2.2

Suggested Questions Discuss the questions in the first paragraph to help launch the problem. This builds off of Problem 2.1 as it raises the question of how great the product will be relative to each factor.

- *Should the product of 1.25 and 0.5 be greater or less than 1? Why?* (Less than 1 because the product of 2 and 0.5 would be exactly 1 but 1.25 is less than 2.)

- *Should the product of 1.25 and 0.5 be greater or less than $\frac{1}{2}$? Why?* (Greater because 1.25 is greater than 1 and the product of 1 and 0.5 would be exactly $\frac{1}{2}$.)

- *How does the product of 125 and 5 relate to the product of 1.25 and 0.5?* (The product of 125 and 5 is greater than the product of 1.25 and 0.5, but it has the same digits. Whether

you are multiplying whole numbers or decimals, you start by multiplying 125 by 5.)

Introduce the problems. You may want to use Question A part (1) as an example to get students started. It might help to notate what is being asked:

- *Question A part (1) is asking:* $N \times 6 = 0.36$. *Is the value of* N *greater or less than 1?* (less than 1)

- *What whole number problem will help us think about this?* ($6 \times 6 = 36$)

- *This problem is not* $6 \times 6 = 36$ *but is related. Will the unknown value that is multiplied by* N *be greater than or less than 1?* (Since the product is less than one, the missing factor must be a fraction or a decimal that is less than one.)

At this point, leave students to think about how to adjust the place value and figure out what the missing factor might be.

Introduce Question B. Use a different value as an example.

- *Let's look at the number 1,560. Give me a number that is a factor of 1,560.* (Some possibilities: 156, 10, 2, 5, 20)

- *Can someone tell me two numbers whose product is 1,560?* (Possible answers: 156×10, 78×20, 39×40, 13×120)

Students' familiarity with factors and multiples from *Prime Time* can be employed here to help them find a pair of numbers whose product is 1,560. They may suggest finding the prime factorization of the number and using it to generate several pairs of numbers whose product is 1,560. The prime factorization is $2 \times 2 \times 2 \times 3 \times 5 \times 13$.

- *We have found several pairs whose product is 1,560. Now can you give me a pair of numbers whose product is 156.0?* (3.9×40, 39×4.0 are two examples.)

Redirect students to B (1). While there are many possible factor pairs that result in 1,344, you will want to suggest that students use the same factor pair to complete each set so that they will be able to look for patterns in their work.

Use a Think-Pair-Share arrangement with this problem.

As students work, ask them how they know what the missing factor is in Question A. Focus on how they knew what place value to use. Observe whether students use fraction form to help them or are starting to use place-value reasoning without having to write out the problem in fraction form.

Suggested Questions For students who struggle to get started, ask:

- *What mathematical sentence could you write to show what the question is asking?* $(6 \times N = \frac{36}{100})$

- *Could you use fact families to help you?* (Yes. The product divided by a factor gives the other factor in a factor pair.)

Be sure students understand what Question B is asking. In Question B you are given the product and have to find a pair of factors with that product. There are lots of answers to each part, but students don't need to give multiple answers. If students use 1 and 1,344 as factors for B(1), suggest they try a different factor pair.

Summarize 2.2

For each set of problems in Questions A–C, have students share their solutions, highlighting and summarizing their strategies. Focus on how students decided what the missing value was and how they knew where to place the decimal.

Suggested Questions Ask:

- *How did you decide what the missing factor was?* (When appropriate, make connections to work with factors and multiples in *Prime Time*.)

- *How did you decide where to put the decimal to get the required product in Question A?*

- *How does part (1) of Question B help with parts (2)–(4)?*

- *In part (1) of Question C, how big is 0.3 compared to 9?* (0.3 is very small and 9 is greater.)

- *Will the missing value be greater or less than 1? Why?* (The missing value is greater than 1. There are a little more than three 0.3's in one whole. There will be at least $3 \times 9 = 27$ three-tenths in 9 wholes.)

- *Let's summarize the different strategies used to find the missing factor.*

Here are some general strategies that students may use to find missing factors:

Fraction Multiplication: With problems like Question A part (1) students may put the problem in fraction form and reason through what the missing whole number factor is and then what the appropriate place value is. If students describe this type of reasoning, notating it for others to see is helpful.

$$\blacksquare \times \frac{6}{1} = \frac{36}{100}$$

Place Value With A (3) one might reason that since one factor is tenths and the product is thousandths, I need hundredths in the missing factor, since tenths × hundredths gives thousandths.

Division With A (2) they may divide 27 by 9 to find the missing factor of 3 and then determine what place value is needed in the 3. For the place value, they may reason that $\frac{1}{10} \times 1 = \frac{1}{10}$, so the factor should be 3.

Counting and Adding Decimal Places The strategy of counting the places behind the decimal in the factors and adding to determine how many places are in the product may surface here as well.

Reflect on the strategies that students offered. Make the observation that across the strategies, students operated with the factors and product as if there were no decimals or as if they were multiplying whole numbers. They then decided where to place the decimal in the product.

Your students have been exploring ways to use fraction multiplication and place value to make sense of decimal multiplication. End the summary by asking:

- *Will someone summarize how fraction multiplication helps us think about decimal multiplication?*

Check for Understanding

- *Find two numbers whose product is 0.060.* (Possible answers: $0.2 \times 0.30, 4 \times 0.015, 0.06 \times 1, 0.003 \times 20, 0.5 \times 0.12$)

- *Now, give a second pair of numbers with the same product, 0.060.*

2.2 Missing Factors

Mathematical Goals

- Use place value to reason about decimal multiplication
- Explore the relationship between factors and products in decimal multiplication

Launch

Discuss the questions in the first paragraph to help launch the problem. You may want to use Question A part (1) as an example to get students started. It might help to notate what is being asked:

- *Question A part (1) is asking $N \times 6 = 0.36$. Is the value of N greater or less than 1?*
- *What whole number problem will help us think about this?*
- *This problem is not $6 \times 6 = 36$, but is related. Will the unknown value that is multiplied by N be greater than or less than 1?*

At this point, leave students to think about how to adjust the place value and figure out what the missing factor might be.

Introduce Question B where students have to find two factors for a given product.

- *Can someone tell me two numbers whose product is 1,560?*

They may suggest finding the prime factorization of the number and using it to generate several pairs of numbers whose product is 1,560.

- *Can you give me a pair of numbers whose product is 156.0?*

Redirect students to Question B part (1). Use a Think-Pair-Share arrangement.

Explore

As students work, ask them how they know what the missing factor is in Question A. Observe whether students use fraction form or place value reasoning.

Be sure students understand what Question B is asking.

Summarize

For each set of problems in Questions A–C, have students share their solutions, highlighting their strategies as they share, and then summarize their strategies. Focus on how students decided what the missing value was and how they knew where to place the decimal. Ask questions like the following:

- *How did you decide what the missing factor was?*
- *How did you decide where to put the decimal to get the required product in Question A?*

Materials
- Student notebooks

continued on next page

continued

- *How does part (1) of B help with parts (2)–(4)?*
- *In part (1) of Question C, how big is 0.3 compared to 9?*
- *Will the missing value be greater than or less than 1? Why?*

Summarize the different strategies used to find the missing factor. Examples of possible strategies are provided in the extended section.

- *Will someone summarize how fraction multiplication helps us think about decimal multiplication?*

Check for Understanding

- *Find two numbers whose product is 0.060.*
- *Give a second pair of numbers with the same product, 0.060.*

ACE Assignment Guide for Problem 2.2

Differentiated Instruction
Solutions for All Learners

Core 7–10, 12–16
Other *Applications* 11; unassigned choices from previous problems

Adapted For suggestions about adapting ACE exercises, see the CMP *Special Needs Handbook*.

Answers to Problem 2.2

A. 1. 0.06. Possible explanation: Since the problem is asking $N \times 6 = 0.36$, you are using six sets of some quantity of hundredths to make 36 hundredths. Six sets of 6 hundredths or 0.06 is 0.36.

2. 3; Possible explanation: $0.9 + 0.9 + 0.9 = 2.7$. It takes 3 sets of 0.9 to make 2.7.

3. 0.03; Possible explanation: Rewrite the decimals in fraction form to say $\frac{15}{10} \times \frac{\blacksquare}{\blacksquare} = \frac{45}{1,000}$. You can see that using $15 \times 3 = 45$ in the numerator and $10 \times 100 = 1,000$ in the denominator lead to $\frac{3}{100}$ or 0.03 as the missing factor.

4. Possible strategy: First ask what you multiply the given number (ignoring the decimal) by to get the product given (ignoring the decimal). Then adjust the decimal place using place value and fractions. For example, with Question A part (1) we can reason that $6 \times 6 = 36$,

and we need 0.36, which is 100 times lesser. Since 6 is a whole number or $\frac{6}{1}$, the other factor needs to be $\frac{6}{100}$ if the product is $\frac{36}{100}$. (Some students may divide fractions to find the answer.)

B. Some possible answers:

1. $42 \times 32 = 1,344$; $24 \times 56 = 1,344$; $4 \times 336 = 1,344$

2. $4.2 \times 32 = 134.4$; $24 \times 5.6 = 134.4$; $0.4 \times 336 = 134.4$

3. $0.42 \times 0.32 = 0.1344$; $0.024 \times 5.6 = 0.1344$; $0.4 \times 0.336 = 0.1344$

4. Possible strategy: I factored 1,344 to find a factor pair. Once I found two factors, I looked at the place value of my product and decided what place values, when multiplied, would result in the place value in the product. For example, if the product was 13.44, I would need hundredths. Since tenths times tenths gives hundreds, I would place decimals into the factors so when multiplied they give the appropriate product. Using tenths times tenths gives the problem 4.2×3.2.

C. 1. 30

2. 200

3. Possible strategy: Since $3 \times 3 = 9$ and 0.3 is 10 times lesser than 3, it will take 10 times as many, or 10×3 is 30 three-tenths to make 9.

2.3 Finding Decimal Products

Goals

- Develop estimation strategies for finding decimal products
- Use estimation as a strategy for finding exact decimal products

This problem introduces estimation as a strategy for determining where to place the decimal in a product. While this is a powerful strategy, it can be difficult to use in some situations; for example, when both factors are less than one. Here we only want to introduce the strategy. In Problem 2.4 you will analyze why different strategies are useful in different situations. You will find that just as with estimation, how you proceed depends upon the actual quantities with which you are working. With decimal multiplication there are often several approaches that make sense.

Launch 2.3

Use the Getting Ready to focus on the idea that there is no one "correct" estimate for a problem. Depending upon the numbers, you can use different approaches. What is important is that an estimate is reasonable. Begin by reading through Jose and Rosa's strategies for the multiplication 2.1 × 1.4.

Suggested Questions Ask:

- *Are both estimates reasonable?* (Yes, in both estimates the quantities are rounded close to the actual quantities.)

- *Which estimate is closer to the actual answer?* (Jose's estimate. In both estimates, 2.1 is represented with a 2. The other value, 1.4, is exact in Rosa's estimate but rounded up in Jose's estimate. Jose's estimate is closer to the actual product.)

- *Even though Rosa's is closer, is it a better estimate?* (No, they both are reasonable.)

Read through Questions A and B of the problem. Point out that in Question B, Julia is using estimation to help her find the actual product, not an estimate. Note that this strategy may have emerged in earlier conversations with students.

Have the students work in pairs but encourage them to try their own ways to estimate products.

Explore 2.3

Look for various estimation strategies that you would like to have come out in the summary. Consider the following questions as you observe students work: Are students using benchmarks? How do they make sense of Question A part (3) where both values are less than 1?

Be sure students understand that Question B is asking to them to consider an approach to finding the actual product using estimation.

Summarize 2.3

Have students share their estimation strategies for Question A. Focus on how different estimates can be reasonable solutions to the same problem even though the estimates use different quantities. After students share their estimates, ask them to help you make a list of general strategies such as benchmark decimals and fractions, whole numbers as benchmarks, and compatible numbers. In addition, highlight that we may change one or both of the quantities in making an estimate.

Suggested Questions For Question B, ask students to explain what they think Julia is thinking. Help students consider how Julia's strategy can help make sense of whether or not a product is reasonable.

- *Does Julia's strategy seem helpful to you in your thinking about how to place the decimal in the product?*

- *How did you use Julia's strategy to find the product of 31.2 × 2.1?* (First, I multiplied the problem as if it were a whole number multiplication problem. $312 \times 21 = 6{,}552$. I estimated 31.2×2.1 to be about 30×2 or 60. Since I rounded down, it will be a little greater than 60 so I have to place the decimal between the fives in 6,552. This gives 65.52, which makes sense according to my estimate.)

- *In Question 2(b), how did Julia's strategy help you to decide if the product should be 1,944.88, 194.48, or 0.194488?* (If we estimate 694.6×2.8 to be about $700 \times 3 = 2{,}100$, or a number in the thousands close to 2,000, then the decimal has to be placed to create a product close to 2,000; or 1,944.88.)

Like other strategies students have used, this strategy begins by using whole number multiplication followed by a method for determining where to place the decimal into the product. At the end of Problem 2.2, a list of decimal multiplication strategies was started. If this strategy was not on the list, add it.

2.3 Finding Decimal Products

Mathematical Goals

- Develop estimation strategies for finding decimal products
- Use estimation as a strategy for finding exact decimal products

Launch

Use the Getting Ready to focus on the idea that there is no one "correct" estimate for a problem. Depending upon the numbers, you can use different approaches. What is important is that an estimate is reasonable. Begin by reading through Jose and Rosa's strategies for the multiplication 2.1×1.4.

- *Are both estimates reasonable?*
- *Which estimate is closer to the actual answer?*
- *Even though Jose's is closer, is it a better estimate?*

Read through Questions A and B of the problem. Point out that in Question B, Julia is using estimation to help her find the actual product, not an estimate. Note that this strategy may have emerged in earlier conversations with students.

Explore

Look for various estimation strategies that you would like to have come out in the summary. Consider the following questions as you observe students: Are students using benchmarks? How do they make sense of Question A part (3) where both values are less than 1?

Be sure students understand that Question B is asking to them to consider an approach to finding the actual product using estimation.

Summarize

Have students share their estimation strategies for Question A. Focus on how different estimates can be reasonable solutions to the same problem even though the estimates use different quantities. After students share their estimates, ask them to help you make a list of general strategies such as benchmark decimals and fractions, whole numbers as benchmarks, and compatible numbers. In addition, highlight that we may change one or both of the quantities in making an estimate.

For Question B, ask students to explain what they think Julia is thinking. Help students consider how Julia's strategy can help make sense of whether or not a product is reasonable.

- *Does Julia's strategy seem helpful to you in your thinking about how to place the decimal in the product?*

Materials
- Student notebooks

continued on next page

Summarize

continued

- *How did you use Julia's strategy to find the product of* 31.2 × 2.1?
- *In Question 2(b), how did Julia's strategy help you to decide if the product should be 1,944.88, 194.488, or 0.194488?*

Like other strategies students have used, this strategy begins by using whole number multiplication followed by a method for determining where to place the decimal into the product. At the end of Problem 2.2, a list of decimal multiplication strategies was started. If this strategy was not on the list, add it.

ACE Assignment Guide for Problem 2.3

Core 17–19, 22–24, 40, 44
Other *Applications* 20, 21; *Connections* 41–43; *Extensions* 49; unassigned choices from previous problems

Adapted For suggestions about adapting ACE exercises, see the CMP *Special Needs Handbook*.
Connecting to Prior Units For suggestions about adapting ACE exercises, see the CMP *Special Needs Handbook*.

Answers to Problem 2.3

A. **1.** Possible estimate: 3.4; round 0.9 to 1 and multiply by 3.4.

   2. Possible estimate: 2.5; round 4.92 to 5 and take half of 5.

   3. Possible estimate: 0.06, using 0.2 × 0.3

   4. Possible estimate: 175, using 25 × 7

B. **1.** Possible explanation: If the product is a little more than one, then the decimal should be placed so the number is "a little more than one." In the number 11,745, if you put the decimals between the ones, the product is a little more than one.

   2. a. N = 65.52

      b. N = 1,944.88

2.4 Factor–Product Relationships

Goals

- Generalize an approach to placing the decimal point into a product that involves counting and adding decimal places

- Consider when various strategies are useful for finding decimal products

- Understand what happens to place value and the position of the decimal when you multiply by powers of 10

- Develop at least one efficient algorithm for multiplying decimals

Through exploration of patterns, students investigate the outcome of multiplication by powers of 10 on the placement of the decimal point in a product. The intention is to help students understand that multiplying by a power of 10 moves the position of the decimal resulting in a change in place value. We want students to confront the notion that multiplying by 10, or a power of 10, adds a zero (or zeros) to a number. This may be true in some cases, but not in all cases involving decimal numbers. For example, multiplying 0.0001 by 10 gives 0.001, while multiplying 1 by 10 adds a zero to give 10.

Using the pattern work, students explore another strategy for finding decimal products: counting the number of decimal places in each factor and adding the decimal places in the factors. The flavor of the conversation should be on choosing an efficient strategy to fit a given situation and recognizing that knowing multiple strategies can be useful.

Launch 2.4

Begin by reviewing place value and introducing the term *power of 10*. Move to introducing the problem.

Suggested Questions Ask students what the difference is between consecutive places.

- *What happens to the value of a digit as you move one place value to the right?* (The value is ten times less.)

- *What happens when you move to the left?* (The value is ten times greater.)

Have students look over the problems in each of the three sets in Question A and describe how they are related.

- *What patterns were used to generate these sets of problems?* (The second factor becomes ten times less as you look down the list of problems. Across the sets, the first factor is ten times less.)

- *What would the next two problems be if we added them to the top of each set of problems? To the bottom?*

Students are asked to use the decimal multiplication strategies they have developed to work on sets of related multiplication problems in Question A. You may want to have students do Question A, summarize, and then launch, explore and summarize Questions B, C, and D. Question B asks students to explore the relationship between the sum of the counted number of decimal places in the factors and the number of decimal places in the product.

Have students work in pairs.

Explore 2.4

If a pair is having trouble getting started, work through the first set of numbers in Question A with them.

Suggested Questions Have them do the work, but ask questions to help guide them.

- *How will each product in Set A relate to the product of 21 and 100?*

- *How can writing the two factors as fractions help you see where the decimal in the answer will be and why?*

- *Can you use a strategy like Julia's to decide where to place the decimal?*

Note whether students are making sense of the counting decimal pattern in Question B.

INVESTIGATION 2

Summarize 2.4

Focus the summary for Question A on the patterns students see in the products and the reasons these patterns make sense.

For Sets A–C, ask questions that focus on comparing the size of the products. For example, multiplying by a progressively lesser power of ten gives a progressively lesser product and multiplying by a progressively greater power of ten gives a progressively greater product.

Suggested Questions

- *Why is the product of* 21×0.001 *less than the product of* 21×0.01? (0.001 means you want one-thousandth of 21 or to partition 21 into 1,000 parts. 0.01 means you want one-hundredth or to partition 21 into 100 parts.)

- *How much less is the product of* 21×0.001 *than* 21×0.01? (It is 10 times less because 0.001 is 10 times less than 0.01.)

Fraction form can also help students see how the product is affected. For example, multiplying by 0.1 or $\frac{1}{10}$ is equivalent to dividing by 10.

- *Why are the products at the bottom of the set less than the products at the top of the set?*

- *Why are the products obtained by multiplying 21 by powers of 10 such as* $\frac{1}{10}, \frac{1}{100} \ldots$ *less than 21?* (Multiplying by a power of 10 (such as $\frac{1}{10}, \frac{1}{100} \ldots$) means you are taking part of 21 and thus decreasing the product. For example, 0.01 means you want one-hundredth of 21. This is the same as dividing 21 into 100 parts and taking 1 part.)

Check for Understanding

- *A student named Linda says that when you multiply by ten it adds a zero to the number. Do you agree? Why or why not?*

- *Can you give an example of a problem where what Linda describes happens?* ($21 \times 10 = 210$)

- *Why do you have to add a zero?* (When you multiply by ten the product is ten times greater.)

- *When you multiply 2.1 times ten the product is ten times greater but you don't add a zero. Why?* (The decimal moves over one place value.)

- *Could it be that the decimal has moved over one place value in* 21×10? (The decimal in 21 isn't written, but it would be "21.0" if it were. If you multiply by ten and get 210, then the decimal is moved over one place to go from "21." to "210.")

Suggested Questions Ask questions that focus on how the decimal moves and how that movement may lead to the need to add a zero, but not always.

- *How is that similar to what happens when you multiply* 0.21×10? (The decimal moves right one place to make the number 10 times greater. You don't have to add a zero because the decimal is between the digits 2 and 1 or 2.1.)

- *What would happen to the decimal if I multiplied* 0.21×100? (The decimal will move right two places to give 21. You won't need to add a zero.)

- *What if you multiply by 1,000?* (Since the decimal moves 3 places to the right and there are only two digits, you have to add a zero for the third place (0.210.). Now the number is 210.

Consider the movement of the decimal and when you do (and do not) add a zero to hold a place when multiplying by a decimal value to get a lesser product.

- *What happens to the decimal when we multiply* 21×0.01? (Since 0.01 is one-hundredth, the decimal will move two places to the left and the product will be 0.21.)

- *What happens to the decimal when we multiply* 21×0.001? (The decimal will move 3 places to the left. You get 0.021. This time you have to insert a zero to make the decimal fall in the right place.)

Return to Linda's question.

- *Do you agree with Linda?* (Sometimes. It depends on what is happening with the decimal. In 21×10 you add a zero since the product is 210. In 2.1×10 you do not since the product is 21. You will add a zero if you need to add a place-value spot to the product.)

Examine Question B.

- *What did you find when you counted decimal places?* (If you add the number of places in each factor it is equal to the number of places behind the decimal in the product.)

• *What do others think?*

• *What happened when you tested the counting decimal places approach on the problems in B(2)?*

Have students demonstrate the approach.

• *Did the products you got when you used the counting decimal places approach agree with the products you got when you used the fraction approach?* (yes)

• *Why might that be?* (The tenths place has one digit after the decimal, the hundredths has two, the thousandths has three, and so on. Tenths are one place past the decimal and hundredths are two places past the decimal.

$$\frac{1}{10} \times \frac{1}{10} = \frac{1}{100}$$

$$0.1 \times 0.1 = 0.01$$

$$0.\blacksquare \times 0.\blacksquare = 0.\blacksquare\blacksquare)$$

Here you want students to begin to focus on how the products are changing and what can account for that. They should be recognizing that the decimal places in the factors show up in the product. Questions B(2) and B(3) have students contrast the place value approach and the fraction approach. Here you want the students to see that the fraction approach shows why the shortcut place-value approach works.

For Question C, ask students to share their approaches to the problems. As students share an approach, ask for other approaches. If students' solutions tend to use one approach, ask about others. If appropriate for your students, push students to talk about why they chose a particular approach and to evaluate others. For example, Julia's estimation approach from 2.3 can be helpful when determining where to place the decimal because the numbers are easy to round to whole number factors that students can easily multiply. Using an estimation approach with very small numbers, like those in Question D(1h), is much more difficult. Here fractions and place value may be easier.

Suggested Questions

• *Do any problems in Question D have the same product?* (Yes, for example, $2.1 \times 1.1 = 0.21 \times 11$. They have the same number of decimal places in the two factors combined.)

• *Can you tell by examining the numbers that they will have the same product?* (Yes, just count the decimal places since the digits are the same.)

• *Can you give another pair of factors that will have the same product?* (21×0.11)

• *Why does* 210×0.011 *have the same product?* (We see that there are three decimal places, but a zero has been added to the 21 to get 210. This adds a decimal place to the left of the decimal. The additional decimal to the left offsets the additional decimal place to the right of the decimal.)

End the summary by describing an algorithm for multiplying decimals. There does not have to be one agreed-upon algorithm. But students should have at least one algorithm that they can use efficiently.

2.4 Factor-Product Relationships

Mathematical Goals

- Generalize an approach to placing the decimal point into a product that involves counting and adding decimal places
- Consider when various strategies are useful for finding decimal products
- Understand what happens to place value and the position of the decimal when you multiply by powers of 10
- Develop at least one efficient algorithm for multiplying decimals

Launch

Introduce the term powers of 10. Students are asked to use the decimal multiplication strategies they have developed to work on sets of related multiplication problems in Question A. You may want to have students do Question A, summarize, and then launch, explore, and summarize Questions B, C, and D. Question B asks students to explore the relationship between the sum of the counted number of decimal places in the factors and the number of decimal places in the product. Have students work in pairs.

In Question A, discuss the patterns students see.

- *What happens to the value of a digit as you move one place value to the right? What happens when you move to the left?*
- *Describe how each of the three sets in Question A are related.*
- *What would the next two problems be if we added them to the top of each set of problems? To the bottom?*

Materials
- Transparency 2.4

Vocabulary
- powers of ten

Explore

If a pair is having trouble getting started, work through the first set of numbers in Question A with them. Have them do the work, but ask questions to help guide them.

- *How will each product in Set A relate to the product of 21 and 100?*
- *How can writing the two factors as fractions help you see where the decimal in the answer will be and why?*
- *Can you use a strategy like Julia's to decide where to place the decimal?*

Note whether students are making sense of the counting decimal pattern in Question B.

Materials
- Labsheet 2.4

Summarize

Examine Question B.

- *What did you find when you counted decimal places?*
- *Did the products you got when you used the counting decimal places approach agree with the products you got when you used the fraction approach? Why might that be?*
- *Do any problems in Question B have the same product? Why?*

Materials
- Student notebooks

continued on next page

- *Can you give another pair of factors that will have the same product?*

In Question D parts (1a) and (1b), Julia's estimation approach can be helpful when determining where to place the decimal because the numbers are easy to round to whole number factors that students can easily multiply. Using an estimation approach with very small numbers, like those in part (1h), is much more difficult. Here fractions and place value may be easier.

End the summary by describing an algorithm for multiplying decimals. There does not have to be one agreed-upon algorithm. But students should have at least one algorithm that they are efficient at using.

ACE Assignment Guide for Problem 2.4

Core 25, 27–31, 33, 45
Other *Applications* 26, 32; *Connections* 50–55; unassigned choices from previous problems

Adapted For suggestions about adapting Exercise 33 and other ACE exercises, see the CMP *Special Needs Handbook*.
Connecting to Prior Units 45: *Covering and Surrounding*

Answers to Problem 2.4

A.

Set A	Set B
21 × 100 = 2,100	2.1 × 100 = 210
21 × 10 = 210	2.1 × 10 = 21
21 × 1 = 21	2.1 × 1 = 2.1
21 × 0.1 = 2.1	2.1 × 0.1 = 0.21
21 × 0.01 = 0.21	2.1 × 0.01 = 0.021
21 × 0.001 = 0.021	2.1 × 0.001 = 0.0021

Set C
0.21 × 100 = 21
0.21 × 10 = 2.1
0.21 × 1 = 0.21
0.21 × 0.1 = 0.021
0.21 × 0.01 = 0.0021
0.21 × 0.001 = 0.00021

B. 1. The number of decimal places in the product is the sum of the number of decimal places to the right of the decimal in the factors.

2. a. 4.05. There is one place behind the decimal in one factor and one place in the other factor for a total of 2 places in the product.

 b. 0.00048. There are three places behind the decimal in one factor and two places in the other factor for a total of 5 in the product.

3. a. $\frac{45}{10} \times \frac{9}{10} = \frac{405}{100}$ and $\frac{4}{1,000} \times \frac{12}{100} = \frac{48}{100,000}$

 b. The counting approach and the fraction multiplication approach lead to the same product. For each place value spot, or tenth, in the factors, the product is adjusted the same number of tenths.

C. Algorithms will vary. Some students may use the fraction multiplication approach while others may prefer the counting decimal places and totaling approach.

D. 1. a. 23.1 **b.** 2.31
  c. 0.231 **d.** 0.0231
  e. 2.31 **f.** 0.0231
  g. 0.00231 **h.** 0.00231

 2. Answers will vary.

Investigation 2

Decimal Times

Here are two everyday situations in which you could multiply decimals.

- How many square feet of carpet do you need to carpet an 11.5 by 12.5 foot room?

- One soccer ball costs $16.79. You buy four soccer balls. How can you find the total cost?

In this investigation you will develop strategies for multiplying decimal numbers. Estimating can help you decide whether a product is reasonable. Changing the form of a number from a fraction to a decimal, or a decimal to a fraction, can help you estimate or find an exact answer.

2.1 Relating Fraction and Decimal Multiplication

You know you can write decimals as fractions. You can also write fractions as decimals. For example, to write $\frac{2}{5}$ as a decimal, first rewrite it as the equivalent fraction $\frac{4}{10}$. Then write $\frac{4}{10}$ as the decimal 0.4.

Notes

_____

_____

_____

_____

The grid on the left below is a tenths grid with one strip shaded. This strip represents $\frac{1}{10}$, or 0.1. On the right, the strip representing 0.1 is divided into 10 squares. The single square with darker shading is $\frac{1}{10}$ *of* $\frac{1}{10}$, or 0.1 × 0.1.

You can extend the horizontal lines to make a hundredths grid. This shows that $\frac{1}{10}$ *of* $\frac{1}{10}$ is one square out of one hundred squares, which is $\frac{1}{100}$, or 0.01 of the whole.

This makes sense because decimals are just fractions written in a different notation. You know that $0.63 = \frac{63}{100}$ and that $0.0063 = \frac{63}{10,000}$. Fraction multiplication can help you with decimal multiplication.

Getting Ready for Problem 2.1

To find the product of 0.3 × 2.3, you can use equivalent fractions.

$$0.3 = \frac{3}{10} \text{ and } 2.3 = 2\frac{3}{10} \text{ or } \frac{23}{10}, \text{ so } 0.3 \times 2.3 = \frac{3}{10} \times \frac{23}{10}$$

- What is the product written as a fraction?
- What is the product written as a decimal?
- How can knowing the product as a fraction help you write the product in decimal form?

Problem 2.1 Relating Fraction and Decimal Multiplication

A. On the next page are some multiplication situations that happen at the Apple-A-Day fruit stand. For each situation, do the following:

- Estimate the product.
- Write the decimals in fraction notation with denominators of 10, 100, 1000, etc.
- Find the exact answer and compare it to your estimate.

22 Bits and Pieces III

Notes _____

_____

_____

_____

1. Ajay buys 1.7 pounds of Red Delicious apples on sale for $0.50 a pound. What is his bill?

2. Kelly buys 0.4 of a pound of Granny Smith apples on sale for $0.55 a pound. What is her bill?

3. Chayton buys Northern Spy apples for his mother's pie. He buys 3.2 pounds at $1.10 a pound. What is his bill?

4. The Apple-A-Day roadside fruit stand sells bunches of wildflowers. The seller wraps each bunch in a sheet of paper with dimensions of 1.5 feet by 1.5 feet. What is the area of the paper?

B. Why does it make sense to use multiplication to solve the situations in Question A?

C. 1. When one factor in a multiplication problem is greater than 1, is the product greater or less than the other factor? Explain.

2. When one factor is less than 1, is the product greater or less than the other factor?

ACE Homework starts on page 28.

2.2 Missing Factors

Suppose you put decimal points into 125×5 to make the problem 1.25×0.5.

- How is the product of 125×5 related to the product of 1.25×0.5?
- Does writing the problem as $\frac{125}{100} \times \frac{5}{10}$ help?

Notes

Problem 2.2 Missing Factors

A. Use what you know about fraction multiplication and place value.

1. What number times 6 gives the product 0.36?

2. What number times 0.9 gives the product 2.7?

3. What number times 1.5 gives the product 0.045?

4. What strategies did you use to solve these problems?

B. Use what you know about decimal multiplication and place value.

1. Find two numbers with a product of 1,344.

2. Find two numbers with a product of 134.4.

3. Find two numbers with a product of 0.1344.

4. What strategies did you use to solve these problems?

C. 1. What number times 0.3 gives the product 9?

2. What number times 0.12 gives the product 24?

3. What strategies did you use to solve these problems?

ACE Homework starts on page 28.

2.3 Finding Decimal Products

Sometimes you don't need to know an actual product. Estimation can help you find an amount that is reasonable.

Sometimes an estimate can help you decide if a computation is correct.

Sometimes an estimate can help you decide where to place the decimal point in an actual product.

Notes

_____

_____

_____

_____

Getting Ready for Problem 2.3

Look at two different estimation strategies for the problem 2.1×1.4.

Jose rounded to whole numbers and fractions: $2 \times 1\frac{1}{2} = 3$

Rosa only rounded one number: $2 \times 1.4 = 2.8$

- Are both estimates reasonable? Which estimate is closer to the actual answer?

Problem 2.3 Finding Decimal Products

A. Estimate each product. Describe how you found your estimate.

1. 0.9×3.4 **2.** 4.92×0.5

3. 0.22×0.301 **4.** 23.87×6.954

B. Julia says that sometimes she uses estimation to decide where to place the decimal in an actual product.

With the problem 0.9×1.305, a reasonable estimate is $1 \times 1.3 = 1.3$. Even 1×1 is a good estimate. I think that the actual product is a little more than 1. When I multiply $9 \times 1,305$ I get 11,745, so I know the actual product is 1.1745.

1. How did Julia use her estimate to find the actual product of 1.1745?

2. Use Julia's estimation strategy to find the product N.

  a. $31.2 \times 2.1 = N$

  b. If $6,946 \times 28 = 194,488$, then $694.6 \times 2.8 = N$.

ACE Homework starts on page 28.

Notes _____

2.4 Factor–Product Relationships

Understanding our place value system depends on knowing about **powers of ten**. The numbers 10; 100; 1,000; 10,000; and so on are powers of ten. You can write these numbers as $10, 10 \times 10, 10 \times 10 \times 10$, and so on OR as $10, 10^2, 10^3 \ldots$.

Our place value system is centered around the units place (ones). A number that is one place to the left of the units place has a value ten times larger. For example, in the number 77, the 7 on the right represents 7 and the 7 on the left represents 7×10, or 70.

As we move to the right we divide by powers of ten.

7 ones

$7 \div 10 \div 10$, OR $7 \div 100$, OR $\frac{7}{100}$

7.77

$7 \div 10$, OR $\frac{7}{10}$

Problem 2.4 Factor–Product Relationships

Estimate before you find an exact answer to the questions below.

A. Record the products in each set in an organized way. Describe any patterns that you see.

Set A	Set B	Set C
21×100	2.1×100	0.21×100
21×10	2.1×10	0.21×10
21×1	2.1×1	0.21×1
21×0.1	2.1×0.1	0.21×0.1
21×0.01	2.1×0.01	0.21×0.01
21×0.001	2.1×0.001	0.21×0.001

26 Bits and Pieces III

STUDENT PAGE

Notes _____

_____

_____

_____

B. In a decimal multiplication problem, there is a relationship between the number of decimal places in the factors and the number of decimal places in the product.

   1. Use your answers to Question A to summarize what you think the decimal place relationship is.

   2. Test the relationship on these two problems:

   a. 4.5×0.9 **b.** 0.004×0.12

   3. a. Write the two problems in part (2) as fractions. Find the product using fraction multiplication.

   b. How does fraction multiplication support the relationship you tested in part (2)?

C. Describe an algorithm you can use to multiply any two decimal numbers.

D. 1. Find the following products using the fact that $21 \times 11 = 231$.

   a. 2.1×11 **b.** 2.1×1.1

   c. 2.1×0.11 **d.** 2.1×0.011

   e. 0.21×11 **f.** 0.021×1.1

   g. 0.021×0.11 **h.** 0.21×0.011

   2. Test the algorithm you wrote in Question C on the problems.

ACE **Homework starts on page 28.**

Notes _____

_____

_____

_____

Applications

Estimate each product.

1. 2.95×14.7 **2.** 0.491×120.2 **3.** 12.45×0.93

4. 0.52×18.3 **5.** 1.262×7.94 **6.** 0.82×0.302

For Exercises 7–12, estimate each product. Then find the exact product using fraction multiplication.

7. 0.6×0.8 **8.** 2.1×1.45 **9.** 3.822×5.2

10. 0.9×1.305 **11.** 5.13×2.9 **12.** 4.17×6.72

13. Sweety's Ice Cream Shop sells ice cream by weight. They charge $2.95 per pound. Suppose your dish of ice cream weighs 0.42 pounds. How much will your ice cream cost?

14. Aaron plans to buy new flooring for his rectangular office. His office is 7.9 meters by 6.2 meters.

   a. How many square meters of floor space does his office have?

   b. Suppose flooring costs $5.90 per square meter. How much will the new flooring cost for Aaron's office?

15. Multiple Choice Which of the products is greater than 1?

   A. 2.4×0.75 **B.** 0.66×0.7 **C.** 9.8×0.001 **D.** 0.004×0.8

16. What number times 9 gives each product?

   a. 45   **b.** 4.5   **c.** 0.45

Find the value of N.

17. $3.2 \times N = 0.96$ **18.** $0.7 \times N = 0.042$ **19.** $N \times 3.21 = 9.63$

20. Multiple Choice Which of the products is the greatest?

   F. 0.6×0.4 **G.** 0.06×0.04

   H. 0.06×0.4 **J.** 0.6×0.04

Notes _____

_____

_____

_____

21. Tom plants corn in 0.4 of his vegetable garden. Of the corn section, 0.75 is early sweet corn and the rest is later-maturing sweet corn.

    a. What part of his garden does Tom plant in early corn? What part does he plant in late corn?

    b. Tom's garden covers 8 acres. How many acres of early corn does he have? How many acres of late corn does he have?

22. Ali sometimes finds it easier to estimate products by using the fractional equivalent of decimal numbers. What do you think he said for the missing numbers below?

"In estimating 0.52×18.3, 0.52 is about 0.5, which as a fraction is the same as ■. And, I can round 18.3 to 18. So, ■ of ■ is ■."

"For 1.262×7.94, I can round the numbers to 1.25×8. Then, 1.25 as a fraction is the same as ■. Since ■ of 8 is 8, and ■ of 8 is 2, the estimate is $8 + 2$, or 10."

23. Ali's classmate, Ahmed, estimates for 0.82×0.302 as follows:

"0.82×0.302 is very close to 0.8×0.3. But, the result of 0.8×0.3 is related to 8×3, which is 24. Since each of 0.8 and 0.3 has only one decimal place, so will their product. The result of 0.8×0.3 should be about 2.4."

Ali immediately said:

"This can't be true. Since both 0.82 and 0.302 are less than 1, their product must also be less than 1. It can't be 2.4!

Who is right? Where did the other person make his mistake?

24. Suppose you estimate the product 0.153×3.4.

    a. Is the result greater than 0.153 or less than 0.153? Why?

    b. Is the result greater than 3.4 or less than 3.4? Why?

Notes _____

_____

_____

_____

25. Suppose you estimate the product 57.132×0.682.

    a. Is the result greater than 57.132 or less than 57.132? Why?

    b. Is the result greater than 0.682 or less than 0.682? Why?

26. Suppose you estimate the product 0.372×0.134.

    a. Is the result greater than 0.372 or less than 0.372? Why?

    b. Is the result greater than 0.134 or less than 0.134? Why?

27. Use the number sentence $78 \times 12 = 936$ to find each product.

    a. 7.8×1.2 **b.** 7.8×0.12

    c. 7.8×0.012 **d.** 0.78×1.2

    e. 0.078×1.2 **f.** 0.0078×1.2

28. Use the number sentence $145 \times 326 = 47{,}270$ to help you solve the following problems.

    a. $1.45 \times 32.6 = \blacksquare$ **b.** $0.326 \times 1{,}450 = \blacksquare$

    c. $\blacksquare \times 32.6 = 472.7$ **d.** $0.0145 \times \blacksquare = 47.27$

29. Use the number sentence $35 \times 123 = 4{,}305$ to help you solve the following problems.

    a. $3.5 \times 123 = \blacksquare$ **b.** $0.35 \times 123 = \blacksquare$

    c. $1.23 \times 0.35 = \blacksquare$ **d.** $3.5 \times \blacksquare = 43.05$

    e. $\blacksquare \times 12.3 = 4.305$ **f.** $3.5 \times 1.23 = \blacksquare$

30. Explain how the number of decimal places in the factors of a decimal multiplication problem relates to the number of decimal places in the product.

31. Explain how you can find the product of 2.7×4.63 if your calculator screen is damaged and does not display numbers with decimals in them.

32. Find each product.

    a. 1.32×10 **b.** 1.32×100

    c. $1.32 \times 1{,}000$ **d.** $1.32 \times 10{,}000$

    e. 12.45×10 **f.** 12.45×100

    g. $12.45 \times 1{,}000$ **h.** $12.45 \times 10{,}000$

Go Online
PHSchool.com
For: Multiple-Choice Skills Practice
Web Code: ame-6254

STUDENT PAGE

Notes _____

_____

_____

_____

STUDENT PAGE

33. Ten-year-old Chi learned a lot of math from his older brother, Shing. One day, Shing tells him that when you multiply a number by 10, "you just add a zero."

   a. With Shing's idea in his mind, Chi says, "To find 10 × 20, I just add a zero. So, 20 + 0 = 20." How would you correct him?

   b. After Chi realizes that "adding zero" actually means "putting an extra zero at the end," he says,

   "10 × 0.02 equals 0.020 by putting the extra zero at the end."

   Is he right this time? How would you rephrase "putting an extra zero at the end" in case the other number is a decimal number? Explain why your suggestion works.

   c. How can you find the result of multiplying by 100; 1,000; or 10,000 using a similar strategy?

Connections

Multiply.

34. $\frac{7}{3} \times \frac{4}{9}$

35. $\frac{2}{5} \times 15$

36. $3 \times \frac{4}{9}$

37. $2\frac{2}{3} \times \frac{1}{2}$

38. $4 \times 2\frac{2}{3}$

39. $1\frac{1}{2} \times 2.3$

Notes _____
_____
_____
_____

40. Midge wants to buy a carpet for her new room. She finds three carpets that she likes, but they are different sizes and have different prices. She writes down the information about their sizes and prices so that she can decide at home.

\ Carpet Comparison			
Carpet	Length (m)	Width (m)	Price (per m²)
A	5.09	4.32	$15.89
B	5.86	3.85	$13.85
C	5.95	3.75	$14.59

   a. Which carpet is the longest?

   b. Which carpet has the greatest area?

   c. What is the total cost of each carpet? Which carpet costs the most? Which carpet costs the least?

Find the area of each shape.

41.

1.735 in.
1.2 in.

42.

28.88 cm
10.64 cm

Homework Help Online
PHSchool.com
For: Help with Exercises 41–44
Web Code: ame-6241

43.

15.63 ft
23.445 ft

44.
6.39 m

45. Find a length and a width for a rectangle with each given area.

   a. 56 ft²   **b.** 5.6 ft²   **c.** 0.56 ft²

Extensions

Find the products.

46. $1.2 \times \frac{31}{40}$ **47.** $0.45 \times 1.7 \times 0.34$ **48.** $0.14 \times 74.3 \times 2.125$

STUDENT PAGE

Notes _____

_____

_____

_____

49. a. Write a fraction equivalent to $\frac{3.7}{23}$ without decimals.

   b. Write a fraction equivalent to $\frac{1.6}{4}$ without decimals.

   c. Use your equivalent fractions from parts (a) and (b) to find the product of $\frac{3.7}{23} \times \frac{1.6}{4}$.

50. Fill in the blanks and put a decimal point where needed to make the calculation complete.

$$
\begin{array}{r}
152\blacksquare \\
\times \quad \blacksquare.9 \\
\hline
1371\blacksquare \\
+ \quad 3\blacksquare48 \\
\hline
4\blacksquare.196
\end{array}
$$

51. Tanisha and Belinda found estimates for the product of 5.2 × 100.4 in two different ways:

Tanisha said: "I round 5.2 to 5. I multiply 5 × 100.4 because I know that 5 × 0.4 is 2. So, my estimation is 500 + 2, or 502."

Belinda said: "I prefer to round 100.4 to 100 and find 5.2 × 100 instead. Moving the decimal point two places to the right, I find the estimation as 520."

Without finding the exact result of 5.2 × 100.4, can you tell whose estimation is closer to the exact answer?

52. Explain why you do not have to align the decimal points when multiplying two decimal numbers.

53. a. Find the area of the square.   **b.** Find the area of each piece within the larger square.

1.5 m
1.5 m

0.5 m   1 m
0.5 m
1 m

   c. Explain how the values you obtained in part (b) are related to your answer to part (a).

Notes _____

_____

_____

_____

54. This morning, Janet was feeling very sleepy toward the end of class when her teacher multiplied two decimal numbers and got 24.9344. Later, when Janet looked at her notebook, she realized that she forgot to put the decimal points of the two numbers in her notebook. Here is what she had written:

a. Where do you think the decimal points should be in the factors?

b. Is there more than one possibility? Explain.

55. On some television game shows, players can lose points for wrong answers. For example, if a player starts with 0 points and gets a 100-point question wrong, he or she has -100 (read as "negative one hundred") points.

a. Suppose a player starts with 0 points and gets three 50-point questions wrong. What is the score?

b. Suppose a player starts with 50 points and gets three 100-point questions wrong. What is the score?

c. Suppose a player starts with 0 points, then gets a 100-point question right and a 200-point question wrong. How many points does this player need to get back to 0 points?

d. A player has 150 points by getting one question right and one question wrong. What are the possible point values of these questions?

Notes _____

_____

_____

_____

Mathematical Reflections 2

In this investigation, you solved problems that involved multiplication of decimals. You looked at the fractional notation of decimals as a way to help you develop strategies for multiplying decimals. You also found patterns in decimal multiplication problems that help you predict the number of decimal places in the answer. The following questions will help you summarize what you have learned.

Think about your answers to these questions. Discuss your ideas with other students and your teacher. Then write a summary of your findings in your notebook.

1. Describe an algorithm for multiplying any two decimal numbers. Use an example to show why your algorithm works.

2. Describe two strategies that you can use to estimate decimal products. Use number sentences to show how your strategies work.

Notes _____

_____

_____

_____

Investigation 2

ACE
Assignment Choices

Differentiated Instruction
Solutions for All Learners

Problem 2.1
Core 1–3, 34–39
Other *Applications* 4–6; *Extensions* 46–48

Problem 2.2
Core 7–10, 12–16
Other *Applications* 11; unassigned choices from previous problems

Problem 2.3
Core 17–19, 22–24, 40, 44
Other *Applications* 20, 21; *Connections* 41–43; *Extensions* 49; unassigned choices from previous problems

Problem 2.4
Core 25, 27–31, 33, 45
Other *Applications* 26, 32; *Extensions* 50–55; unassigned choices from previous problems

Adapted For suggestions about adapting Exercise 33 and other ACE exercises, see the CMP *Special Needs Handbook*.
Connecting to Prior Units 34–39: *Bits and Pieces II*; 40–45: *Covering and Surrounding*

Applications

1.–12. There is more than one way to estimate the products. Some possible answers:

1. Rounding numbers to 3×15, we get 45.

2. Rounding numbers to 0.5×120, we find half of 120, which is 60.

3. 0.93 is almost 1. So, the result will be about 12.

4. Considering half of 18, we find 9.

5. Considering one and a quarter of 8, we find 10.

6. Think of 0.8×0.3 instead. Since $8 \times 3 = 24$, the estimate would be 0.24.

7. Estimate: 0.5 ($\frac{1}{2} \times 1 = \frac{1}{2}$)
Exact result: 0.48 ($\frac{6}{10} \times \frac{8}{10} = \frac{48}{100} = 0.48$)

8. Estimate: 3 ($2 \times \frac{3}{2} = 3$)
Exact result: 3.045 ($\frac{21}{10} \times \frac{145}{100} = \frac{3,045}{1,000} = 3.045$)

9. Estimate: 20 ($4 \times 5 = 20$)
Exact result: 19.8744 ($\frac{3,822}{1,000} \times \frac{52}{10} = \frac{198,744}{10,000} = 19.8744$)

10. Estimate: 1.3 ($1 \times 1.3 = 1.3$)
Exact result: 1.1745 ($\frac{9}{10} \times \frac{1,305}{1,000} = \frac{11,745}{10,000} = 1.1745$)

11. Estimate: 15 ($5 \times 3 = 15$)
Exact result: 14.877 ($\frac{513}{100} \times \frac{29}{10} = \frac{14,877}{1,000} = 14.877$)

12. Estimate: 28 ($4 \times 7 = 28$)
Exact result: 28.0224 ($\frac{417}{100} \times \frac{672}{100} = \frac{280,224}{10,000} = 28.0224$)

13. $0.42 \times \$2.95 = \$1.239$ (you will be charged $1.24)

14. a. 48.98 m^2
b. $288.98

15. A

16. a. 5   **b.** 0.5   **c.** 0.05
17. N = 0.3   **18.** N = 0.06   **19.** N = 3
20. F

21. a. 0.3 of his whole garden is planted in early corn. 0.1 of his whole garden is planted in late corn.
b. 2.4 acres of early corn and 0.8 acres of late corn.

22. In estimating 0.52×18.3, 0.52 is about 0.5, which as a fraction is the same as $\frac{1}{2}$. And, 18.3 can be rounded to 18. So, $\frac{1}{2}$ of 18 is 9.
For 1.262×7.94, I can round the numbers to 1.25×8. Then, 1.25 as a fraction is the same as $1\frac{1}{4}$. Since $\frac{4}{4}$ of 8 is 8, and $\frac{1}{4}$ of 8 is 2, the estimate is $8 + 2$ or 10.

23. Ali is right. If two positive numbers are both less than 1, then their product is always less than 1. Ahmed's mistake is to put in only one decimal place. We need to take into account both decimal places of 0.8 and 0.3. Since each number has one decimal place, the result will have 1 + 1 = 2 decimal places. So, the correct estimation is 0.24.

24.a. Greater than 0.153. This is because 3.4 is more than 1 and we can consider this product as saying "*take a little more than 3 copies of 0.153 added to each other,*" which definitely gives more than 0.153 itself.

b. Less than 3.4. This is because 0.153 is less than 1. If we imagine the fractional equivalent of 0.153, which will be less than a whole, the product is less than a whole of the number 3.4.

25. a. Less than 57.132. Consider the product 0.682 × 57.132. Since 0.682 is less than 1, by the same reasoning as in 24b, the product will be less than 57.132.

b. Greater than 0.682. By the same reasoning as in 24a, we are looking at more than 57 copies of 0.682 added to each other.

26. a.–b. Both numbers are less than 1, so, using the same idea as in 24b, we can say that we are looking at less than a whole of both numbers. As a result, the product is going to be less than both numbers.

27. a. 9.36   b. 0.936
    c. 0.0936   d. 0.936
    e. 0.0936   f. 0.00936

28. a. 47.27   b. 472.7
    c. 14.5   d. 3260

29. a. 430.5   b. 43.05
    c. 0.4305   d. 12.3
    e. 0.35   f. 4.305

30. The sum of the number of decimal places in each factor is equal to the number of decimal places in the product. (Note: This is the case when you don't count "extra" zeros. For example, in 3.2 × 5.30, you have one decimal place in 3.2 and one in 5.3.) The multiplication 3.2 × 5.3 has one decimal place in each factor for a total of 2 places. The product will need to have two places. Since 32 × 53 = 1,696, the product of 3.2 × 5.3 will be 16.96.

31. We can multiply 27 by 463 and insert three decimal places. Because 2.7 is tenths and 4.63 is hundredths, the product will be a decimal with a thousandths in the answer. Thus, from 27 × 463 = 12,501, we see that 2.7 × 4.63 must be 12.501.

32. a. 13.2   b. 132
    c. 1,320   d. 13,200
    e. 124.5   f. 1,245
    g. 12,450   h. 124,500

33. a. "Add a zero," in this context, means "place a zero on the right side of number." So, we put a zero at the end of 20 and get 200. The zero is holding the decimal in a certain place. In this case the decimal was moved one place to the right by multiplying by 10, and the zero is "*added*" or "*put*" on the end of the 20 to make it 200.

b. He is wrong again, because placing a zero on the right side of a number is done when the multiplication causes the decimal to move enough places that it is necessary to show that the place value is used but it represents 0 of that place. For example, in 20 there are 2 tens and 0 ones. Since 0.02 was multiplied by 10, moving the decimal one to the right makes the product ten times greater. A digit already exists in the place-value spot to the right, so just move the decimal over one place to get 0.2.

c. Each time you multiply by 10 the decimal is moved one place to the right to make the value ten times greater. If you multiply by 100 you move the decimal two places right since 100 is 10 × 10, or has two tens. Since 1,000 is 10 × 10 × 10 or three tens, the number will be 1,000 times greater and the decimal moves 3 to the right. You only add zeros when there are not enough existing digits to move the decimal where it is needed.

Connections

34. $\frac{28}{27}$ or $1\frac{1}{27}$ 35. 6

36. $\frac{4}{3}$ or $1\frac{1}{3}$ 37. $\frac{4}{3}$ or $1\frac{1}{3}$

38. $\frac{32}{3}$ or $10\frac{2}{3}$ 39. $\frac{69}{20}$ or $3\frac{9}{20}$ or 3.45

40. a. Carpet C is the longest.

    b. Carpet B has the greatest area (about 22.56 m^2).

    c. Carpet A is $349.40, Carpet B is $312.47, Carpet C is $325.54. Carpet A is the most expensive. Carpet B is the least expensive.

41. 2.082 in.^{2}

42. 153.6416 cm^2

43. 366.44535 ft^2

44. $\approx$ 128.28 m^2

45. a. Possible answer: length = 8 ft and width = 7 ft

    b. Possible answers: length = 0.8 ft and width = 7 ft or length = 8 ft and width = 0.7 ft

    c. Possible answers: length = 0.8 ft and width = 0.7 ft, length = 8 ft and width = 0.07 ft, or length = 0.08 ft and width = 7ft

Extensions

46. 0.93   **47.** 0.2601   **48.** 22.10425

49. a. $\frac{3.7}{23} \times \frac{10}{10} = \frac{37}{230}$

    b. $\frac{1.6}{4} \times \frac{10}{10} = \frac{16}{40}$ or $\frac{2}{5}$

    c. $\frac{3.7}{23} \times \frac{1.6}{4} = \frac{37}{230} \times \frac{16}{40} \left(\frac{2}{5}\right) = \frac{592}{9,200} \left(\frac{37}{575}\right)$
    (or 0.0643478)

50.
```
  15.24
×  2.9
 13716
 3048
44.196
```

51. Belinda's answer is closer to the exact answer. Tanisha rounds 5.2 to 5 and loses 0.2 × 100.4 which is more than 20. Belinda rounds 100.4 to 100 and loses 0.4 × 5.2 which is much less than what Tanisha loses.

52. When multiplying two decimal numbers, we multiply the two numbers as if they do not have any decimal points. Only at the end of multiplication, we count the total number of decimal places in the factors and locate the decimal point in the result accordingly. (Note: This is analogous to the fact that we do not need common denominators to multiply common fractions, while we do to add them.)

53. a. 2.25 m^2

    b. 0.25 m^2, 0.5 m^2, 0.5 m^2, and 1 m^2

    c. The sum of the areas of part (b) is equal to the area of part (a):
    0.25 + 0.5 + 0.5 + 1 = 2.25.

54. a.–b. Three possibilities: 0.487 × 51.2 or 4.87 × 5.12 or 48.7 × 0.512

    Note that the total number of decimal places in the factors must be 4 for each possibility.

55. a. −150 points

    b. −250 points

    c. She needs +100 points.

    d. Answers will vary. Possible answer: She got a 200-point question right and a 50-point question wrong.

Possible Answers to Mathematical Reflections

1. Write each decimal as a fraction with a power of 10 (10, 100, 1,000, etc.) in the denominator. If the number is greater than 1, write it as an improper fraction. Multiply the numerators of these fractions to get the numerator of the product. Multiply the denominators of these fractions to get the denominator of the product. Write the product as a decimal. For example, 0.6 × 0.12 is equivalent to $\frac{6}{10} \times \frac{12}{100} = \frac{72}{1,000}$. You can rename the product $\frac{72}{1,000}$ as a decimal or 0.072.

2. One strategy is to round one or both decimal numbers to the nearest whole number and multiply those values. For example, 3.9 × 4.098 is approximately 16 because 4 × 4 = 16. Another strategy involves benchmarks. For example, in the problem 0.49 × 12.3, 0.49 can be approximated with the benchmark $\frac{1}{2}$ and 12.3 as 12. $\frac{1}{2}$ of 12 is 6.

Investigation 3 The Decimal Divide

Mathematical and Problem-Solving Goals

- Choose between division, multiplication, addition, or subtraction as an appropriate operation to use to solve a problem

- Use models and the context to find solutions to division problems

- Estimate to find approximate solutions

- Use the relationship between decimals and fractions to develop and understand decimal division

- Use knowledge about fractions and place value to understand and develop algorithms for dividing decimals

- Use efficient algorithms for dividing decimals

- Explore the inverse relationship between multiplication and division in fact families

- Understand and predict the decimal representation of a fraction (terminating or repeating)

Summary of Problems

Problem 3.1 Deciphering Decimal Situations

Students evaluate situations to determine which operation is appropriate to use and solve division problems using models and other approaches that are sensible.

Problem 3.2 The Great Equalizer: Common Denominators

Students use the common denominator approach to fractions as a way to make sense of decimal division.

Problem 3.3 Exploring Dividing Decimals

Problem 3.3 continues to use fraction division in looking at place value. Students examine related decimal division problems that lead to a related whole number division problem with the same solution.

Problem 3.4 Representing Fractions as Decimals

Students investigate how to predict which fractions will have a terminating or a repeating decimal form.

	Suggested Pacing	Materials for Students	Materials for Teachers	ACE Assignments
All	$5\frac{1}{2}$ days			
3.1	1 day			1–4, 28–30
3.2	$1\frac{1}{2}$ days		Transparency 3.2	5–14, 31
3.3	$1\frac{1}{2}$ days		Transparency 3.3	15–24, 32–34, 41–43
3.4	1 day	Calculator		25–27, 35–40
MR	$\frac{1}{2}$ day			

A Note on Division

Division is challenging for many students in elementary school. If their elementary backgrounds are weak in this area, you may need to give some additional homework with whole numbers and decimals to help them become more proficient with up to a two-digit number divided into a three-digit number. It is reasonable to move to a calculator when the students understand and can do smaller divisions by hand. Students seem to more fully understand the operation of division itself by thinking through their struggles to do some problems by hand.

You can help the students remember (or, if this is a new idea, learn) that the long division algorithm is based on finding how many groups the size of the divisor that are contained in the dividend. The steps of the algorithm show the removing of groups the size of the divisor until the amount left is less than the quantity needed to make another group. The quotient is the count of groups contained in the dividend, plus the amount left over, or the remainder. Sometimes the remainder is written as a fraction or decimal to show the part of another group that you can make.

You might give the class a whole number problem and a fraction division problem, like $450 \div 23$ and $\frac{3}{5} \div \frac{1}{2}$ to do as a warm-up. Discuss their solutions. You might also revisit the sharing and grouping types of division situations from *Bits and Pieces II*. Have students describe a situation that fits the division $15 \div 5 = 3$. This will get the students' heads back into division of whole numbers and fractions and give you a chance to clear up any confusion.

Mathematics Background

For background on estimation and algorithm development of decimal division as well as terminating and repeating decimal and fraction forms, see pages 5–6.

3.1 Deciphering Decimal Situations

Goals

- Choose between division, multiplication, addition, or subtraction as an appropriate operation to use to solve a problem

- Use models and the context to find solutions to division problems

- Estimate to find approximate solutions

Students are given contextual problems to solve. The context itself can help students to make sense of meaning of the operations. In Question A the problems are decimal division problems. The numbers have been carefully chosen so students can use models, diagrams, and understanding of division as an operation to find solutions. In Question B students are asked to determine which operation is needed to solve a problem. Students are asked to estimate solutions rather than solve the problems.

Launch 3.1

Describe and clarify Questions A and B in Problem 3.1. Be sure students understand the expectations. Remind students that they can use models or diagrams to help them solve the problems.

Have students work in pairs.

Explore 3.1

As students work, ask them about the number sentences they wrote for Question A part (3).

Suggested Questions

- *What does the 3.2 and the 0.4 in Question A part(1) represent?* (3.2 represents the total ounces of prosciutto Ricardo bought and 0.4 is how many ounces goes on a sandwich.)

- *How did you decide what operation is needed?*

Look for various approaches to Question A that can be shared in the summary. Note how students estimate in the various situations in Question B. Assess how much support the students will need with division estimation in the summary and throughout the investigation.

Summarize 3.1

Have students share their solutions, explanations, or diagrams, and their number sentences to Question A.

Suggested Questions

- *Why is division appropriate for these problems?* (There is a quantity that is being partitioned or divided into parts of equal size.)

- *Are the division situations in A(1) and A(2) sharing or grouping?* (sharing)

Have students talk about what their solutions represent. Move to Question B and have students share their estimates. Focus on how students knew which operation was appropriate.

- *How did you decide what operation to use?* (I thought about the context and looked at whether I had to find how many groups you could make of a certain size. This was the case in part (3) where you needed to know how many 75 cents are in $12.45. If I needed to find out how two numbers differed, I used subtraction as in part (2). But here you had to add first to find out the total amount of money that you have. Part (1) was about finding a total where the pieces were the same. This is what multiplication does. So here you can multiply 5.25 by 5 or add 5.25 five times and get the answer.)

End the summary by having students describe general characteristics of addition, subtraction, multiplication, and division situations.

3.1 Deciphering Decimal Situations

Mathematical Goals

- Choose between division, multiplication, addition, or subtraction as an appropriate operation to use to solve a problem
- Use models and the context to find solutions to division problems
- Estimate to find approximate solutions

Launch

Describe and clarify Questions A and B in Problem 3.1. Be sure students understand the expectations. Remind students that they can use models or diagrams to help them solve the problems. Have students work in pairs.

Explore

As students work, ask about the number sentences they wrote.

- *What does the 3.2 and the 0.4 in Question A part(1) represent?*
- *How did you decide what operation is needed?*

Look for various approaches to Question A that can be shared in the summary. Note how students estimate in the various situations in Question B. Assess how much support the students will need with division estimation in the summary and throughout the investigation.

Summarize

Have students share their solutions, explanations or diagrams, and number sentences to Question A.

- *Why is division appropriate for these problems?*
- *Are the division situations in A(1) and A(2) sharing or grouping?*

Have students talk about what their solutions represent. Move to Question B and have students share their estimates. Focus on how students knew which operation was appropriate.

- *How did you decide what operation to use?*

End the summary by having students describe general characteristics of addition, subtraction, multiplication, and division situations.

Materials
- Student notebooks

ACE Assignment Guide for Problem 3.1

Differentiated Instruction
Solutions for All Learners

Core 1–4, 28, 29
Other *Connections* 30

Adapted For suggestions about adapting Exercises 1–4 and other ACE exercises, see the CMP *Special Needs Handbook*.
Connecting to Prior Units 28: *Bits and Pieces I*; 29: *Bits and Pieces II*

Answers to Problem 3.1

A. **1.** $3.2 \div 0.4 = 8$ sandwiches; approaches will vary. Students might draw diagrams or use repeated addition to see how many times 0.4 goes into 3.2.

2. $11.6 \div 0.25 = 46.4$ quarter-pound hamburgers; approaches will vary. Students might draw pictures or use fraction reasoning. For example, there are four $\frac{1}{4}$'s in one pound. So $11 \times 4 = 44$ plus two more quarters in 0.6 with 0.4 of another left.

3. For A(1): $3.2 \div 0.4 = 8$ sandwiches.

For A(2): $11.6 \div 0.25 = 46.4$ quarter-pound hamburgers.

4. Students may reason that there are 46 quarters in 11.6 and 0.4 left over, which means you can make 0.4 of another patty.

B. **1.** Multiplication. Possible estimate: $5 \times 5 = 25$ ounces

2. Addition and subtraction. Possible estimate: $22.50 + 15 = 37.50$; Stacey does not have enough money to buy the shoes.

3. Division. Possible estimate: $12 \div 1 = 12$; since a trip is a little less than $1, she can get a few more than 12 trips, possibly about 15. Another strategy is to make sets of 0.75. Since there are two 0.75's in 1.50, there are 4 groups of 0.75 in $3. Since 3 goes into 12 four times, and each $3 is four trips, $4 \times 4 = 16$. With this strategy, students argue for multiplication as the appropriate operation.

Goals

- Use the relationship between decimals and fractions to develop and understand decimal division

- Use the common denominator approach to fraction division as a strategy to help understand and develop an algorithm for dividing decimals

- Relate the emerging division algorithm to place value understanding

In this investigation we look directly at what happens when we rewrite both the dividend and the divisor of a problem in decimal form into fraction form. Then we write the fractions in common denominator form to find an equivalent division problem with whole number dividend and divisor. This effectively produces a whole number division problem with the same answer as the original decimal problem. This strategy can also help students make sense of the standard long division algorithm with decimals. Rather than the mystery of why we "move" decimal points and then divide, this approach gives the students solid reasons for why this short cut makes sense.

The dividend and divisor of each decimal division problem in Question A has the same place value, tenths or hundredths. In fraction form, the fractions have a common denominator. The dividend and divisor of the problems in Question B have different place values, and when working in fraction form, will need to be renamed to have common denominators.

Launch 3.2

Introduce the vocabulary and the ways of indicating division in the introduction to Problem 3.2. The words that refer to the numbers involved in a division are not in and of themselves important, but they do make communication about a problem much clearer. Use your own judgment about whether to stress these or not. Students will see the different forms for representing division and need to recognize what

is meant. Use the Getting Ready to introduce fraction division as a strategy for decimal division.

Suggested Questions Ask:

- *What does the division 3.25 ÷ 0.5 mean?* (How many 0.5's are in 3.25?)

- *Describe a real-life situation that this decimal division problem could represent.* (How many half-meter sticks can be cut from a stick 3.25 meters long?)

- *What is a reasonable estimate for 3.25 ÷ 0.5?* ($3 \div \frac{1}{2} = 6$)

- *Is this estimate greater than or less than the actual answer?* (Less than because you replaced the dividend with a lesser number but kept the divisor the same.)

- *Why is the quotient for this problem going to be greater than 1?* (The dividend is greater than the divisor. There is more than one half in 3 wholes.)

Introduce the use of fraction division as a strategy for decimal division.

Suggested Questions

- *Are the problems 3.25 ÷ 0.5, $\frac{325}{100} \div \frac{5}{10}$, and $\frac{325}{100} \div \frac{50}{100}$ equivalent?* (yes)

- *Why does the quotient to $\frac{325}{100} \div \frac{50}{100}$ equal the quotient to 325 ÷ 50?* ($\frac{325}{100} \div \frac{50}{100}$ means the same thing as 325 hundredths ÷ 50 hundredths. The hundredths is a label telling how large the parts are.)

- *What does the quotient $6\frac{1}{2}$ or 6.5 represent?* (There are 6 whole 0.5's and half of a 0.5 in 3.25. Some students may say that the answer represents how many 50 hundredths, 0.50, are in 325 hundredths, 3.25.)

- *Can someone show the 6.5, or $6\frac{1}{2}$, groups of $\frac{1}{2}$?*

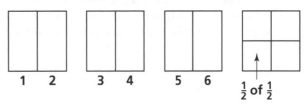

INVESTIGATION 3

Do not go for closure here. Students will explore fraction division as they work on this problem and Problem 3.3.

Move the students into the Explore by going over the kinds of problems that they are being asked to solve. You may want to plan a discussion with the class after Question B so that you know all students are moving in the right direction.

Have students work in pairs or small groups

Explore 3.2

As you circulate, troubleshoot for those students that need help dividing fractions using the common denominator approach. In addition, ask questions that focus on the interpretation of division, a strategy for carrying out the operation, and the meaning of the quotient.

Summarize 3.2

Have students share their estimates and their division work.

The problems in Question A have common denominators. As students share their fraction computation problems, ask questions that help students focus on how a related whole number division problem results from this approach. At some point in their work across Problems 3.2 and 3.3, we want students to realize that when you divide equal-size units, such as 16 tenths by 8 tenths, the quantities (16 and 8) are what are acted upon. When the unit of measure (tenths) is the same for the dividend and the divisor, it does not affect the numerical outcome.

Suggested Questions

- *What whole number division problem is related to 42 tenths ÷ 21 tenths?* (42 ÷ 21)

- *In Question A part (3), what does the quotient 5.5 mean when the problem is 0.44 ÷ 0.08 and when it is 44 ÷ 8?* (In the decimal division it means that there are 5 and a half groups of size 8 hundredths in 0.44. In 44 ÷ 8 it means that there are 5 and a half groups of size 8 in 44.)

Depending upon the progress of your students you may want to ask:

- *What would be the remainder in each problem?* (For 0.44 ÷ 0.08 the remainder would be 0.04 and for 44 ÷ 8 the remainder will be 4.)

- *How is this remainder related to the decimal answer of 5.5?* (The groups you are making in 0.44 ÷ 0.08 are of size 0.08. A remainder of 0.04 is exactly half of 0.08, so you can make another half of a group. In 44 ÷ 8 the groups you are making are of size 8. The remainder is exactly half of 8 so you can make another half of a group.)

- *Can you use the solution to 44 ÷ 8 to solve 4.4 ÷ 0.8 without writing the dividend and divisor as fractions?* (Yes. This problem is in tenths. 44 tenths divided by 8 tenths has the same answer as 44 ÷ 8.)

Look carefully at Question B with the class. This should reinforce the ideas that the students developed in Question A. When summarizing Question B, ask students to share how they found equivalent fractions in order to make common denominators. Here the denominators are not always naturally the same. Adjustments have to be made in Sets 2 and 3.

In Set 2 the second problem raises a new complication for some students. The whole number problem with the same denominator is 288 ÷ 1800. Since students seem to do less division in the elementary grades, this may be a challenge since using long division raises the issue of adding a decimal and additional zeros to carry out the algorithm. However, there are other ways to handle this. You can allow students to do the computation with calculators or suggest that they look at equivalent fractions to see whether an alternative form helps. Here the fraction string might look like the following:

$$\frac{288}{1,800} = \frac{144}{900} = \frac{72}{450} = \frac{12}{75} = \frac{4}{25} = \frac{16}{100} = 0.16$$

Have students share their solutions to parts C and D. The focus is on rewriting decimal division problems as fractions with common denominators and then replacing the problem with equivalent whole-number problems. Test any new approaches that arise and if appropriate, add them to the algorithms that students are developing.

- *Let's start by collecting all of the strategies we have explored for dividing decimals on the board. Raise your hand if you have one to contribute.* (Be sure the fraction algorithm and variations surface. Also make sure students describe ways to change the form of the problem into one that has the same answer but a whole-number dividend and divisor.)

- *Let's try our ideas on a problem. Give me an example of a problem.* (Write the problem on the board and have the class work it out.)

- *Do the ideas work?* (Ask for evidence or explanation that they work.)

- *What does Question C mean when it says "an easier division problem?"* (It means a problem where the dividend and the divisor are whole numbers.)

Check for Understanding

- *Write each of the following as an equivalent division problem with a whole-number dividend and divisor and find the quotient.*

  a. *3.6 ÷ 0.08*   b. *3,600 ÷ 0.08*
  (360 ÷ 8 = 45; 360,000 ÷ 8 = 45,000)

- *Describe your strategy for finding the equivalent division problem.* (Various answers. Some students may begin to move decimal points simultaneously, in the dividend and the divisor, keeping numerical equivalence, until they have two whole numbers. Others will still rely on fractions with common denominators to help find the related whole-number division.)

Mathematical Goals

- Use the relationship between decimals and fractions to develop and understand decimal division
- Use the common denominator approach to fraction division as a strategy to understand and develop an algorithm for dividing decimals
- Relate the emerging division algorithm to place value understanding

Launch

Introduce the vocabulary in Problem 3.2. Use the Getting Ready to introduce fraction division as a strategy for decimal division.

- *What does the division 3.25 ÷ 0.5 mean?*
- *What is a reasonable estimate for 3.25 ÷ 0.5?*
- *Why is the quotient for this problem going to be greater than 1?*

Introduce the use of fraction division as a strategy for decimal division.

- *Are the problems 3.25 ÷ 0.5, $\frac{325}{100} \div \frac{5}{10}$, and $\frac{325}{100} \div \frac{50}{100}$ equivalent?*
- *What does the quotient $6\frac{1}{2}$ represent?*
- *Why does the quotient to $\frac{325}{100} \div \frac{50}{100}$ equal the quotient to 325 ÷ 50?*

This last question serves to get ideas out for consideration. Do not go for closure here.

Go over the kinds of problems that they are being asked to solve. Have students work in pairs or small groups.

Materials
- Transparency 3.2

Vocabulary
- divisor
- dividend
- quotient

Explore

As you circulate, troubleshoot for those students who need help dividing fractions using the common denominator approach. Ask questions that focus on the interpretation of division, a strategy for carrying out the operation, and the meaning of the quotient.

Summarize

Have students share their estimates and their division work.

Ask questions that help students focus on how a related whole-number division problem results from this approach. At some point in their work across Problems 3.2 and 3.3, we want students to realize that when you divide equal-size units, such as 16 tenths by 8 tenths, the quantities (16 and 8) are what are acted upon. When the unit of measure (tenths) is the same for the dividend and the divisor, it does not affect the outcome.

- *What whole-number division problem is related to 42 tenths ÷ 21 tenths?*

Materials
- Student notebooks

continued on next page

- *Can you use the solution to 44 ÷ 8 to solve 4.4 ÷ 0.8 without writing the dividend and divisor as fractions?*

Have students share their solutions to parts C and D. The focus is on rewriting decimal division problems as fractions with common denominators and then replacing the problem with equivalent whole number problems. Test any new approaches that arise and, if appropriate, add them to the algorithms that students are developing.

Check for Understanding

- *Write each of the following as an equivalent division problem with a whole-number dividend and divisor and find the quotient.*
- a. *3.6 ÷ 0.08*   b. *3,600 ÷ 0.08*
- *Describe your strategy for finding the equivalent division problem.*

ACE Assignment Guide for Problem 3.2

Differentiated Instruction
Solutions for All Learners

Core 5–14
Other *Connections* 31; unassigned choices from previous problems

Adapted For suggestions about adapting ACE exercises, see the CMP *Special Needs Handbook*.

Answers to Problem 3.2

A. 1. About 2; $4.2 \div 2.1 = \frac{42}{10} \div \frac{21}{10}$ which has the same answer as $42 \div 21 = 2$.

2. About 8; $16.1 \div 2.3 = \frac{161}{10} \div \frac{23}{10}$ which has the same answer as $161 \div 23 = 7$.

3. About 5; $0.44 \div 0.08 = \frac{44}{100} \div \frac{8}{100}$ which has the same answer as $44 \div 8 = 5.5$.

B. 1. Set 1: $\frac{464}{10} \div \frac{58}{10}, \frac{464}{100} \div \frac{58}{100}$

Set 2: $\frac{288}{10} \div \frac{18}{10}, \frac{288}{100} \div \frac{1,800}{100}$

Set 3: $\frac{1,750}{10} \div \frac{125}{10}, \frac{1,750}{1,000} \div \frac{125}{1,000}$

2. Set 1: $464 \div 58$ for both

Set 2: $288 \div 18; 288 \div 1,800$

Set 3: $1,750 \div 125$ for both

3. Problems in Set 1 lead to the same quotient, as do the problems in Set 3. The problems in Set 2 do not have the same whole-number division equivalent. The quantities being divided are different in each problem.

4. Set 1: 8 and 8

Set 2: 16 and 0.16

Set 3: 14 and 14

Answers on checking against their predictions will vary.

C. 1. $\frac{785}{10} \div \frac{91}{10}$

2. Since the size of the pieces or the place value is the same, divide the numerators, $785 \div 91$.

D. Possible explanation: If there are decimals in the dividend and divisor you can write an equivalent division problem by multiplying both the dividend and the divisor by the same power of ten until both terms are whole numbers. You can write the decimals as fractions and divide the numerators. The fraction approach explains why the approach of counting decimal places works.

1. 25   **2.** 25   **3.** 2500

Exploring Dividing Decimals

Goals

- Use knowledge about computation with fractions to understand algorithms for division with decimals

- Use place value to develop an algorithm for division with decimals

- Develop and use efficient algorithms for dividing decimals

- Explore the inverse relationship between multiplication and division in fact families

This problem gives additional practice for the emerging algorithm or shortcut method for decimal division developed in Problem 3.2. The focus here moves away from representing the dividend and the divisor as a fraction toward representing decimal division problems as equivalent whole number division problems in order to be more efficient in dividing decimals. This work uses patterns and place value as the foundation. Here the students also write fact families and use this as a strategy for finding missing factors. The students are building strategies and ways of thinking that help with solving linear equations.

Launch 3.3

In this problem, students will examine sets of division problems that look related, but may not be related. The whole number problems may be different, leading to different quotients. Students will also confront division situations where the quotient is less than one.

First review the different ways to write division problems. Have the students look at, but not solve, the problems in Question A parts (1) and (2). Ask them to predict whether the problems in each set will have the same solution.

Move on to Question C and perhaps do a whole number fact family, such as $48 \div 6 = 8$, together with the class as a review. Ask students to explain the relationship between multiplication and division. Their ideas may not be well formed now, but return to this idea in the summary. You

would like students to see that multiplication and division are inverse operations.

This problem can be done in small groups, but each student should do each problem first and then share ideas within their group.

Explore 3.3

As students work, make sure to ask about how the problems are alike and different. Ask "why" questions of all the groups. The point is to build a solid foundation of understanding for division of decimals. This also gives another chance for students to practice division of fractions if they have problems.

Suggested Question An excellent standard question to ask is:

- *Can you write another problem with the same answer?*

If students are struggling, you might want to stop and summarize Question A before working on the rest of the problem.

Summarize 3.3

Focus on two ideas in the summary. First, there is a whole-number division problem that has the same numerical answer as the original decimal problem. The reason you can move to whole numbers is that the problem has a dividend and a divisor that are written in the "same size pieces."

Once students have found the quotient for the various computation problems in Question A (1), focus on the additional problems in Question A (2) and why they do not all have the same solution.

Suggested Question Ask:

- *How did you decide that 2,750 ÷ 5.5 had a different quotient than the other two problems in A(2)?* (Problems (a) and (c) have the same form when written as fractions with common denominators. Question B has a different whole number representation. Parts (a) and (c) are numerically equivalent to 2,750 ÷ 550, but (b) is numerically equivalent to 27,500 ÷ 55, or 2,750 ÷ 5.5.)

Second, focus on looking for patterns that allow students to do the decimal division without the intermediate step of changing to fraction form. However, encourage students who get confused to return to using the decimal form and equivalent fractions.

Suggested Questions

- *On your paper quickly solve $0.75 \div 2.5$. How did you solve the problem?* (If you rename 2.5 as 2.50, you have the problem $0.75 \div 2.50$. This is the same as 75 hundredths divided by 250 hundredths, or $75 \div 250$. Factoring out 25 from 75 and 250 leaves a solution of $\frac{3}{10}$, or 0.3.)

- *Can you decide whether the answers to two or more related division problems will be the same without working out the quotient?* (Yes, you can just look at whether the place values of the dividend and the divisor in the two problems are the same or can be multiplied by the same power of ten [10, 100, 1,000, etc.] to make them the same.)

Some students may continue to use the fraction form of the decimal division problem to decide. Others may be able to decide without using fraction form. They focus on the place value and equivalent decimals instead of equivalent fractions. For example, in $0.75 \div 2.5$, the 0.75 is hundredths and 2.5 is tenths. If you want to have the same place value (common denominator) you can rename 2.5 as 2.50 and now you have 75 hundredths divided by 250 hundredths. This is equivalent to the whole number problem $75 \div 250$.

For Question B, have students share a few problems they have written. Examine each closely with the class to be sure it is a division situation that calls for the division $1.75 \div 0.5$.

Move to fact families and examine the relationship between multiplication and division.

- *How are multiplication and division related?*

- *Who can show a fact family for $0.84 \div 0.06 = 14$?*

- *How does the fact family help solve for a missing factor, divisor, or dividend?*

Question C is likely to be hard for students. However, becoming comfortable with fact families gives a way to build a foundation for solving linear equations of the form $x \times 4.5 = 18$, $18 \div x = 4.5$, or $18 \div 4.5 = x$. These are all part of a fact family showing the multiplication/division relationships among three numbers. Examine the fact family to see which member makes it easiest to find the value of x that makes the sentences true. In this case $18 \div 4.5 = x$ is the fact that makes it easy to find the value of x.

Have students show their fact families for parts (1) and (2) and then ask for strategies they used to write the fact families. The key is recognizing that in the equation $N \div 0.8 = 3.5$, the question being asked is what number divided by 0.8 gives 3.5. The N represents the product of the factors 0.8 and 3.5. A related multiplication problem for this would be $3.5 \times 0.8 = N$.

In the problem $2.75 \div N = 5.5$, 5.5 and N are a pair of factors for 2.75. Since we know one factor, we can divide 2.75 by that known factor to find the value of N that makes the sentence correct. $2.75 \div 5.5 = N$. This is one of the facts in the fact family.

Question D is an application problem that uses computation with decimals. It can be assigned as homework if you are short on time.

3.3 Exploring Dividing Decimals

Mathematical Goals

- Use knowledge about computation with fractions to understand algorithms for division with decimals
- Use place value to develop an algorithm for division with decimals
- Develop and use efficient algorithms for dividing decimals
- Explore the inverse relationship between multiplication and division in fact families

Launch

First review the different ways to write division problems. Have the students look at, but not solve, the problems in Question A parts (1) and (2). Ask them to predict whether the problems in each set will have the same solution.

This problem can be done in groups, but each student should do each problem first and then share ideas within their group. Review a fact family for $\times$ and $\div$.

Materials
- Transparency 3.3

Explore

As students work, make sure that you look at their thinking about how the problems are alike or different. Be sure to ask "why" questions. The point is to build a solid foundation of understanding for division of decimals. An excellent standard question to ask is:

- *Can you write another problem with the same answer?*

If students are struggling, you might want to stop and summarize Question A before working on the rest of the problem.

Summarize

Focus on two ideas in the summary. First, there is a whole-number division problem that has the same numerical answer as the original decimal problem. The reason you can move to whole numbers is that the problem has a dividend and a divisor that are written in the "same size pieces."

For Question B, have students share a few word problems they wrote for $1.75 \div 0.5$.

Second, focus on looking for patterns that allow students to do the decimal division without the intermediate step of changing to fraction form. However, encourage students who get confused to return to using the decimal form and equivalent fractions.

Materials
- Student notebooks

continued on next page

Summarize

continued

Some students may use the fraction form of the decimal division problem to decide. Others may be able to decide without using fraction form.

- *Can you decide whether the answers to two or more related division problems will be the same without working out the quotient?*

Move to fact families and examine the relationship between multiplication and division.

- *How are multiplication and division related?*
- *Who can show a fact family for 0.84 ÷ 0.06 = 14?*
- *How does the fact family help solve for a missing factor, divisor, or dividend?*

See the extended Summarize for an in-depth discussion and possible answers.

After summarizing Question C, return to the algorithm developed in Problem 3.2 and revise as needed. Question D can be assigned as homework if you are short on time.

ACE Assignment Guide for Problem 3.3

Differentiated Instruction
Solutions for All Learners

Core 15–19, 22–24
Other *Applications* 20–21, *Connections* 32–33, *Extensions* 34, 41–43; unassigned choices from previous problems

Adapted For suggestions about adapting ACE exercises, see the CMP *Special Needs Handbook*.

Answers to Problem 3.3

A. 1. a. 5   **b.** 5   **c.** 5

     d. Any problem whose dividend and divisor have the same fraction representation as the problems above will work. Some examples are $0.55\overline{)2.75}$ and $5{,}500\overline{)27{,}500}$.

     2. a. 0.5   **b.** 500   **c.** 0.5

     The three computations do not all have the same solutions. However, a and c do have the same solution because the dividend and the divisor of (c) are $\frac{1}{10}$ the dividend and divisors of (a). In part (b), the dividend is 100 times greater than the dividend of part (a) and the divisor is $\frac{1}{10}$ as great as the divisor of part (a).

B. Possible problem: I have 1.75 pounds of mints. If I put 0.5 pound in a serving bowl, how many bowls will I need? The dividend of 1.75 is the total pounds, the divisor of 0.5 is pounds per serving or how much each bowl should have in it. The quotient is the number of bowls I can fill with 0.5 pound in each, if I have a total of 1.75 pounds.

C. 1. $0.06 \times 14 = 0.84$, $14 \times 0.06 = 0.84$; $0.84 \div 14 = 0.06$; and $0.84 \div 0.06 = 14$

     2. a. N = 2.8 since you know that N = 3.5 × 0.8;

     b. N = 0.5 since you know that 2.75 ÷ 5.5 = N.

D. 1. Measurements are always approximations. Possibly some groups were more careful than others.

     2. first week: 3.36 cm; second week: 8.02 cm

     3. 4.66 cm

Representing Fractions as Decimals

Goal

- Understand and predict the decimal representation of a fraction (terminating or repeating)

To add to the story of the relationship between fractions and decimals, this optional problem explores the kinds of decimal representation fractions can have. Students already know from *Bits and Pieces I* that a fraction can be interpreted as an indicated division and represented as a decimal. They have also observed that some fractions have a decimal representation that terminates in a finite number of digits, such as $\frac{1}{2} = 0.5$, while others have decimal representations that are infinite repeating decimals, such as $\frac{1}{3} = 0.33333. \ldots$ What we explore in this problem is how to predict which fractions will have terminating decimal forms and which will have repeating decimal forms.

Launch 3.4

You can use the examples in the introductory text to get the students thinking about the decimal forms of fractions. Introduce the terms *terminating* and *repeating* so that students have a way of talking about what they observe.

Use the bulleted questions to introduce equivalent fractions with the same decimal representation. These questions do not need closure. They are meant to set the stage for the problems students will work on.

Suggested Questions

- *Why do fractions like $\frac{1}{2}$ and $\frac{1}{4}$ have terminating decimal forms?* (You can write them as a fraction that is out of a power of ten. For example, $\frac{1}{2} = \frac{5}{10}$, or 0.5.)

- *Are there fractions equivalent to $\frac{1}{2}$ and $\frac{1}{4}$ that have 10; 100; 1,000; etc. as their denominator?* (Yes. $\frac{1}{2} = \frac{5}{10} = \frac{50}{100} = \frac{500}{1,000}$. The numerator has to be half of the denominator. These are all equivalent. Adding zeros to the right (on the end) of a decimal number doesn't change

the value. The fractions with the greater denominator have more parts in the whole and since they are smaller size parts you need more, but each is equivalent to five tenths.)

- *What are some other fractions besides $\frac{1}{2}$ and $\frac{1}{4}$ with terminating decimals?* ($\frac{1}{8} = 0.125$)

- *How do you know $\frac{1}{8}$ can be expressed as a terminating decimal?* ($\frac{1}{8}$ is half of $\frac{1}{4}$ and half of 0.25 is 0.125.)

- *Is there another way to show that $\frac{1}{8}$ is a fraction with a power of ten in the denominator?* (The decimal 0.125 means the fraction would be $\frac{125}{1,000}$. You can multiply 8 by a number that gives a power of ten. For example, $8 \times 125 = 1,000$, so you have $\frac{1}{8} \times \frac{125}{125} = \frac{125}{1,000}$. You can write the fraction as a decimal with a power of ten in the denominator.)

- *What other fractions are equivalent to the decimal 0.125?* ($\frac{2}{16}$ or any fraction that is equivalent to $\frac{1}{8}$.)

Read through the problem parts making sure students understand what is expected. The question of determining whether a given fraction will have a repeating or terminating decimal form is the goal of the problem. If you think that you will not have time for students to explore all parts of the problem in class, assign Questions A–C and give Questions D and E for homework to be discussed in the next class period. However, if you split the problem, have a summary of the parts completed before the class ends. This will help students make sense of the remaining parts of the problem at home.

Working in small groups works well for this problem. Using a calculator is also appropriate.

Explore 3.4

As you circulate, ask questions that focus students on examining the factors of the denominators of the fractions they are considering.

Ask students if they can find fractions equivalent to ones they are considering that have smaller denominators. When you look for equivalent forms of fractions, you often need to consider the factors of the denominator to be sure you have all fractions with smaller denominators. (Some students will understand this as simplifying the fraction form.)

Ask what kinds of factors are in the denominators of the simplified forms of the fractions that have terminating decimals. Students will begin to see that those that have only 2's and 5's in their denominators in simplified form have terminating decimals. Those with other factors in their denominators in simplest form will have repeating decimal forms.

Summarize 3.4

Have students share examples of fractions that they found that have terminating decimal representations. Then do the same thing with fractions that have a repeating decimal representation. Record these on the board or overhead.

Terminating Decimal Forms					
$\frac{1}{2}$	$\frac{2}{8}$	$\frac{3}{12}$	$\frac{1}{4}$	$\frac{2}{4}$	$\frac{3}{4}$
$\frac{2}{5}$	$\frac{1}{8}$	$\frac{5}{10}$	$\frac{12}{48}$	$\frac{3}{5}$	...

Repeating Decimal Forms					
$\frac{1}{3}$	$\frac{1}{9}$	$\frac{1}{11}$	$\frac{2}{6}$	$\frac{1}{27}$	$\frac{2}{3}$
$\frac{5}{11}$	$\frac{10}{12}$	$\frac{5}{6}$	$\frac{1}{7}$	$\frac{4}{12}$	...

Go back through the list with the class and circle the ones in lowest terms. Those fractions that are not in lowest terms will have a lowest form equivalent that will have the same decimal form. You might add any lowest form fractions to the chart that the class finds in the process of analyzing the fractions in the chart.

Suggested Questions Now examine the set of fractions in lowest terms and ask:

- *The question we want to answer is, "How can you tell if a fraction has a repeating or a terminating decimal form?"*

- *What kinds of denominators of fractions in lowest terms seem to give terminating or repeating decimal forms?*

- *Look at our list carefully and see whether you can come up with some ideas.*

After students have a few minutes to think about this, ask for conjectures or explanations.

You want the class to notice that the answer depends on the denominator in lowest terms and whether it is a factor of a power of 10. If they still haven't figured out what is going on, look at the prime factorizations of 10, 100, 1,000, etc. so that you highlight that powers of 10 have only 2's and 5's as prime factors. Since any fraction (whole number numerator and denominator) with a power of 10 in the denominator has a terminating decimal form, students should begin to notice that the fractions in the terminating list have only 2's and 5's in their lowest form denominators. With 2's or 5's or a combination of 2's and 5's, you can always find a fraction form with a power of 10 in the denominator and, thus, find a terminating decimal form. Otherwise the decimal form is repeating.

No matter how hard you try, $\frac{1}{3}$ does not equal a fraction with a power of 10 as the denominator, whereas for $\frac{1}{2}$ there is the form $\frac{5}{10}$, which is equivalent to 0.5.

Mathematical Goals

- Understand and predict the decimal representation of a fraction (terminating or repeating)

Launch

Use the examples in the introductory text to get the students thinking about the decimal forms of fractions. Introduce the terms terminating and repeating so that students have a way of talking about what they observe.

Use the bulleted questions to introduce equivalent fractions with the same decimal representation. These questions do not need closure. They are meant to set the stage for the problems students will work on.

Read through the problem parts making sure students understand what is expected. The question of determining whether a given fraction will have a repeating or terminating decimal form is the goal of the problem.

Working in small groups works well for this problem. Using a calculator is also appropriate.

Vocabulary
- repeating decimal
- terminating decimal

Explore

As you circulate, ask questions that focus students on examining the factors of the denominators of the fractions they are considering. Ask students if they can find fractions equivalent to ones they are considering that have smaller denominators. When you look for equivalent forms of fractions, you often need to consider the factors of the denominator to be sure you have all fractions with smaller denominators. (Some students will understand this as simplifying the fraction form.)

Summarize

Have students share examples of fractions that they found that have terminating decimal representations and those that have a repeating decimal representation. Record these on the board or overhead.

Go back through the list with the class and circle the ones in lowest terms. Those fractions that are not in lowest terms will have a lowest form equivalent that will have the same decimal form. Add any additional lowest form fractions to the chart that the class finds.

Now examine the set of fractions in lowest terms and ask:

- *How can you tell if a fraction has a repeating or a terminating decimal form?*
- *What kinds of denominators of fractions in lowest terms seem to give terminating or repeating decimal forms?*

Materials
- Student notebooks

continued on next page

You want the class to notice that the answer depends on the denominator in lowest terms and whether it is a factor of a power of 10. If they still haven't figured out what is going on, look at the prime factorizations of 10, 100, 1,000, etc. so that you highlight that powers of 10 have only 2's and 5's as prime factors. With 2's or 5's or a combination of 2's and 5's you can always find a fraction form with a power of 10 in the denominator and, thus, find a terminating decimal form. Otherwise the decimal form is repeating.

ACE Assignment Guide for Problem 3.4

Core 27
Other *Applications* 25, 26; *Extensions* 35–40; unassigned choices from previous problems

Adapted For suggestions about adapting ACE exercises, see the CMP *Special Needs Handbook*.

Answers to Problem 3.4

A. 1. 0.4; terminating

  2. 0.375; terminating

  3. 0.8333333 . . . ; repeating

  4. 3.5; terminating

  5. 0.080808 . . . ; repeating

  6. $\frac{2}{5} = \frac{4}{10}; \frac{3}{8} = \frac{375}{1,000}; \frac{35}{10} = \frac{35}{10}$

B. 1. Possible answer: $\frac{3}{20}$ or $\frac{6}{30}$

  2. $\frac{3}{20} = \frac{6}{40} = \frac{9}{60} = \frac{15}{100}$ or $\frac{6}{30} = \frac{12}{60} = \frac{30}{150} = \frac{2}{10}$

  3. 0.15 and 0.2

  4. The decimal form for each member of the set of equivalent fractions is the same.

C. 1. Possible answer: $\frac{35}{100}$

  2. Possible answer: $\frac{21,456}{10,000}$

  3. Possible answer: $\frac{89,050}{1,000}$ or $\frac{8,905}{100}$

  4. Possible answers: $\frac{214,560}{100,000}$ or $\frac{21,456}{10,000}$

  5. The fractions are equivalent even though they differ by a factor of 10 in the numerator and denominator.

D. 1. Possible answer: $\frac{1}{9}, \frac{10}{15},$ or $\frac{2}{7}$

  2. No. There is no equivalent form with a power of 10 in the denominator. In the simplest form of the fraction, terminating decimals only have 2's and/or 5's in the prime factorization of the denominator. Repeating decimals will have factors other than 2 or 5.

E. A repeating decimal has only one form as a decimal, even though we might write it in different ways, for example, 0.3333 . . . or $0.\overline{3}$ or $0.3\overline{3}$ and so on. If the fraction has a terminating decimal, you can add zeros after the decimal point at the end of a decimal representation and produce another that looks different, but has the same value. To tell whether a fraction has a terminating or repeating decimal representation, examine it in its simplest form. Fractions with terminating decimals only have 2's and/or 5's in the prime factorization of the denominator. Fractions with repeating decimals will have factors other than 2 or 5 in the denominator. (Note: Even though we can represent a repeating decimal in written form, if you wish to operate with a repeating decimal you should use fraction form if you want an exact solution. Terminating decimals are exact representations and we can operate with them in either form.)

The student edition pages for this
investigation begin on the next page.

Notes

Investigation 3

The Decimal Divide

In this investigation, you will use what you learned about fraction division in *Bits and Pieces II* to make sense of decimal division. You will estimate a solution to a division problem and you will learn to divide decimals.

3.1 Deciphering Decimal Situations

Use what you know about decimal, fraction, and whole number operations to find solutions for each problem.

Problem 3.1 Deciphering Decimal Situations

A. In a grocery store, all of the scales measure in decimals. Explain or draw diagrams to show your reasoning for the following situations.

1. Ricardo buys 3.2 ounces of a sliced Italian ham called prosciutto (pruh SHOO toh) to make sandwiches. Each sandwich uses one 0.4-ounce slice of prosciutto. How many sandwiches can he make?

2. Ms. Difanis buys 11.6 pounds of hamburger for a cookout. How many quarter-pound (0.25) burgers can she make?

3. Write a number sentence that shows the operations you would use to find your solutions in parts (1) and (2).

4. The answer to part (2) is not a whole number. What does the answer mean?

Notes _____

_____

_____

_____

B. Examine each situation. Decide what operation to use and then estimate the size of the answer.

1. Ashley eats five 5.25-ounce slices of watermelon in a contest at the picnic. How many ounces of watermelon does she eat?

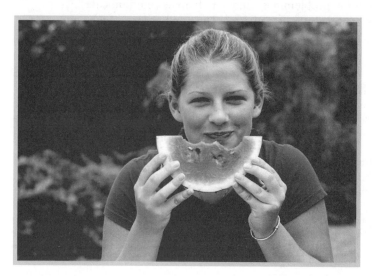

2. Stacey needs $39.99 for a pair of sneakers. She has $22.53 in her savings and a $15 check from babysitting. Can she buy the shoes?

3. Li Ming's allowance for transportation is $12.45. How many times can she ride the bus if it costs $0.75 a trip?

ACE Homework starts on page 43.

Notes _____

_____

_____

_____

3.2 The Great Equalizer: Common Denominators

Each number in a division problem has a name to help us communicate. The number you are dividing by is the **divisor.** The number into which you are dividing is the **dividend.** The answer is the **quotient.**

$$18 \quad \div \quad 3 \quad = \quad 6$$

$$\text{dividend} \quad \div \quad \text{divisor} \quad = \quad \text{quotient}$$

Remember that there are three ways to write a division problem:

Number Sentence: $22 \div 88$ Fraction: $\frac{22}{88}$ Long Division: $88\overline{)22}$

You know that decimals can be thought of as fractions. You can use what you already know about dividing fractions to help you figure out a way to divide decimals.

Getting Ready for Problem 3.2

- What does the division $3.25 \div 0.5$ mean?
- What is a reasonable estimate for $3.25 \div 0.5$?

To find the answer to $3.25 \div 0.5$, think of the decimals as fractions.

$$3.25 \div 0.5 = \frac{325}{100} \div \frac{5}{10}$$
$$= \frac{325}{100} \div \frac{50}{100}$$

This is the same as 325 hundredths $\div$ 50 hundredths $= 6\frac{1}{2}$, or 6.5.

- Why does the quotient to $\frac{325}{100} \div \frac{50}{100}$ equal $325 \div 50$?
- What does the answer to the division mean?

38   Bits and Pieces III

STUDENT PAGE

Notes

Problem 3.2 **Using Common Denominators to Divide Decimals**

A. Estimate each quotient. Write each dividend and divisor in fraction form with common denominators. Use fraction division.

1. $4.2 \div 2.1$ **2.** $16.1 \div 2.3$ **3.** $0.44 \div 0.08$

B. **1.** Rewrite the problems in each set below as fraction division problems with common denominators.

Set 1	Set 2	Set 3
$46.4 \div 5.8$	$28.8 \div 1.8$	$175 \div 12.5$
$4.64 \div 0.58$	$2.88 \div 18$	$1.75 \div 0.125$

2. Write the whole number division problem that corresponds to each problem you wrote in part (1).

3. Without solving, decide if the problems within each set lead to the same quotient. Explain.

4. Solve the problems and check your predictions.

C. Luis thinks that he can use long division with decimals just as he does with whole numbers. He writes $78.5 \div 9.1$ as $9.1\overline{)78.5}$, but he does not know what to do with the decimals.

1. Use fractions to represent Luis' dividend and divisor.

2. Replace the division problem with an easier division problem that has the same answer. Check that the answer is the same.

D. Describe how to rewrite a decimal division problem so that the division is easier and the answer is the same. Check your ideas by solving these division problems.

1. $15\overline{)375}$

2. $3.75 \div 0.15$

3. $37.5 \div 0.015$

ACE Homework starts on page 43.

Investigation 3 The Decimal Divide   **39**

Notes _____
_____
_____
_____

3.3 Exploring Dividing Decimals

You have explored several different situations involving decimal division. You will use your ideas to describe a way to do decimal division.

Problem 3.3 Exploring Dividing Decimals

A. 1. Solve each division problem.

  a. $5.5\overline{)27.5}$ **b.** $550\overline{)2{,}750}$ **c.** $0.055\overline{)0.275}$

  d. Write another division problem that belongs to this set.

  2. Do these problems all have the same solution? Why or why not?

  a. $55\overline{)27.5}$ **b.** $5.5\overline{)2{,}750}$ **c.** $0.55\overline{)0.275}$

B. Write a word problem for $1.75 \div 0.5$. Explain what the dividend, divisor, and quotient mean in your problem.

C. 1. Write the complete multiplication-division fact family for $0.84 \div 0.06 = 14$.

  2. Find the value of N. Writing a fact family may help.

  a. $N \div 0.8 = 3.5$ **b.** $2.75 \div N = 5.5$

D. Five science lab teams measure the height of a plant at the end of week 1 and week 2. See their measurements below.

Week	Team 1	Team 2	Team 3	Team 4	Team 5
1	3.4 cm	3.25 cm	3.3 cm	3.5 cm	3.35 cm
2	7.95 cm	7.8 cm	8 cm	8.15 cm	8.2 cm

  1. All the teams measured the same plant. Why are the measurements different?

  2. Find the mean (average) of the teams' measurements for each week.

  3. Using each week's mean, how much did the plant grow from the first week to the second week?

ACE Homework starts on page 43.

40 Bits and Pieces III

Notes _____

_____

_____

_____

3.4 Representing Fractions as Decimals

In *Bits and Pieces I*, you learned that you can express any fraction with a whole number numerator and a whole number denominator as a decimal by dividing the numerator by the denominator.

$\frac{1}{2} = 0.5$ $\frac{1}{4} = 0.25$

$\frac{1}{3} = 0.333333\ldots$ $\frac{1}{11} = 0.090909\ldots$

The fractions $\frac{1}{2}$ and $\frac{1}{4}$ have decimal representations that end or terminate.

Decimals like these are called **terminating decimals.** Notice that $\frac{1}{3}$ and $\frac{1}{11}$ have decimal representations that repeat over and over. Decimals like these are called **repeating decimals.**

This is a repeating decimal.

You know that decimals are easy to write as fractions with 10, 100, 1000, etc. in the denominator.

$0.23 = \frac{23}{100}$ $0.7 = \frac{7}{10}$ $0.070 = \frac{70}{1000}$

You can see that fractions with 10, 100, 1000, etc. in their denominators have terminating decimal forms.

- Why do fractions like $\frac{1}{2}$ and $\frac{1}{4}$ also have terminating decimal forms?
- Are there fractions equivalent to $\frac{1}{2}$ and $\frac{1}{4}$ that have 10, 100, 1000, etc. as their denominators?

Investigation 3 The Decimal Divide   **41**

Notes _____

_____

_____

_____

Problem 3.4 Representing Fractions as Decimals

A. Write each fraction as a decimal. Tell whether the decimal is terminating or repeating. If it is repeating, tell which digits repeat.

1. $\frac{2}{5}$ **2.** $\frac{3}{8}$ **3.** $\frac{5}{6}$ **4.** $\frac{35}{10}$ **5.** $\frac{8}{99}$

6. For the fractions in parts (1)–(5) that have terminating decimal forms, try to find an equivalent fraction that has 10, 100, 1000, etc. as the denominator.

B. 1. Find two other fractions that have a terminating decimal form.

2. For each fraction you found in part (1), write three fractions that are equivalent.

3. Find the decimal form for the fractions you found in part (2).

4. What do you notice about the decimal form for a set of equivalent fractions?

C. Find a fraction that is equivalent to each of the following terminating decimals.

1. 0.35 **2.** 2.1456 **3.** 89.050 **4.** 2.14560

5. Explain how your answers in part (2) and part (4) compare.

D. 1. Find three fractions that have repeating decimal forms.

2. Can you find an equivalent form for any of these fractions that has 10, 100, 1000, etc. in the denominator? Why or why not?

E. Describe any differences in the forms of repeating and terminating decimals that you have found.

ACE Homework starts on page 43.

Notes

_____

_____

_____

_____

Applications

For Exercises 1–4, decide what operation is needed to answer the question. Explain.

1. Akiko's dog has three puppies. They weigh 2.6 pounds, 2.74 pounds, and 3.1 pounds. How much more does the heaviest puppy weigh than the lightest puppy?

2. Angie is making wreaths to sell at a craft show. She has 6.5 yards of ribbon. Each wreath has a bow made from $1\frac{1}{3}$ yards of ribbon. How many bows can she make?

3. Mrs. Doran has three grandchildren. She takes them to lunch where kids' meals are $2.95 each. How much will the three kids' meals cost?

4. Loren is putting brick along both edges of the 21-meter walkway to his house. Each brick is 0.26 meters long. Loren is placing the bricks end to end. How many bricks does he need?

★ **Kids' Menu** ★

Chicken Nuggets . . $2.95
P.B. & J. $2.95
Hot Dog $2.95
Mac & Cheese $2.95

5. Draw a diagram to show how to find the solution to 2.6 ÷ 0.4. Explain what the quotient means.

6. Will the quotient in each be greater than or less than 1? Explain.

   a. 19.36 ÷ 3.893   **b.** 0.962 ÷ 0.3

   c. 5.3 ÷ 11.07   **d.** 0.072 ÷ 0.09

For Exercises 7–12, write the decimals as fractions. Then find each quotient.

7. 4.5 ÷ 0.9   **8.** 0.6 ÷ 0.12   **9.** 1.2 ÷ 0.5

10. 0.18 ÷ 0.03   **11.** 22.5 ÷ 1.5   **12.** 3.42 ÷ 0.19

13. Find the quotient of 22.4 ÷ 0.5 and describe what the quotient means.

14. Explain how finding the quotient of 401 ÷ 5 can help you find the quotient of 40.1 ÷ 0.5.

Investigation 3 The Decimal Divide   **43**

Notes _____

_____

_____

_____

Compute each quotient.

15. $12.012 \div 5.6$ **16.** $45.13 \div 0.125$

17. $1.2 \div 4.8$ **18.** $1.99 \div 10$

For Exercises 19 and 20, compute the quotients. Look for patterns in your answers.

19. **a.** $36 \div 12$ **b.** $3.6 \div 12$ **c.** $3.6 \div 1.2$
        d. $3.6 \div 0.12$ **e.** $3.6 \div 120$ **f.** $0.36 \div 0.012$

20. **a.** $124 \div 32$ **b.** $1,240 \div 320$ **c.** $12,400 \div 3,200$
        d. $12,400 \div 3.2$ **e.** $1.24 \div 3.2$ **f.** $1.24 \div 0.32$

21. **a.** Find the quotient of $0.37 \div 10$.

   b. How is the quotient similar to 0.37? How is it different?

   c. Divide the quotient from part (a) by 10. How is the quotient similar to 0.37, and how is it different?

   d. In general, what do you think happens to a decimal number when you divide it by 10?

22. **a.** Write two related problems with the same answer as $48 \div 12$. Explain.

   b. Write two related problems with the same answer as $4.8 \div 0.12$.

Find the value of N, and then write the complete multiplication-division fact family.

23. $0.42 \div N = 0.6$ **24.** $N \div 0.5 = 6.4$

25. Find the decimal equivalent for each of these fractions:

   a. $\frac{2}{6}$ **b.** $\frac{13}{39}$ **c.** $\frac{5}{15}$

   d. Describe the relationship between the fractions and their decimal equivalents.

26. Find the decimal equivalent for each fraction or mixed number:

   a. $\frac{11}{9}$ **b.** $1\frac{6}{27}$

   c. Describe the relationship between the fraction or mixed number and its decimal equivalents.

44 Bits and Pieces III

STUDENT PAGE

Notes

27. a. Copy the table below, and write each fraction as a decimal.

Fraction	Decimal
$\frac{1}{9}$	▦
$\frac{2}{9}$	▦
$\frac{3}{9}$	▦
$\frac{4}{9}$	▦
$\frac{5}{9}$	▦
$\frac{6}{9}$	▦
$\frac{7}{9}$	▦
$\frac{8}{9}$	▦

b. Describe the pattern you see in your table.

c. Use the pattern to write decimal representations for each of these fractions. Use your calculator to check your answers.

   i. $\frac{9}{9}$ **ii.** $\frac{10}{9}$ **iii.** $\frac{15}{9}$

d. What fraction is equivalent to each of these decimals? Note that 1.222 . . . can be written as $1 + 0.22 \ldots$.

   i. 1.2222 . . .   **ii.** 2.7777 . . .

Connections

28. For parts (a)–(d), copy the number line and label the marks.

e. Explain your strategy for parts (a)–(d).

STUDENT PAGE

Notes _____

_____

_____

_____

29. Multiple Choice Which quotient is greater than 1?

A. $\frac{1}{4} \div \frac{3}{8}$ **B.** $\frac{19}{5} \div 5$ **C.** $1\frac{2}{3} \div 2\frac{2}{9}$ **D.** $3 \div \frac{19}{7}$

Homework Help **O**nline
PHSchool.com
For: Help with Exercise 29
Web Code: ame-6329

30. For parts (a)–(c), use the table. Give evidence to support your conclusions. You may want to make a table of the differences between each pair of consecutive years.

Men's Springboard Diving		
Year	**Winner (country)**	**Score**
1960	Gary Tobian (USA)	170
1964	Kenneth Stizberger (USA)	150.9
1968	Bernie Wrightson (USA)	170.15
1972	Vladimir Vasin (USSR)	594.09
1976	Phil Boggs (USA)	619.52
1980	Aleksandr Portnov (USSR)	905.02
1984	Greg Louganis (USA)	754.41
1988	Greg Louganis (USA)	730.8
1992	Mark Lenzi (USA)	676.53
1996	Ni Xiong (CHINA)	701.46
2000	Ni Xiong (CHINA)	708.72
2004	Bo Peng (CHINA)	787.38

a. Between what consecutive Olympic years did the greatest change in winning score occur?

b. Between what consecutive Olympic years did the next greatest change in winning score occur?

c. Between what consecutive Olympic years did the least change in winning score occur?

d. What is the average of Greg Louganis's scores?

31. a. Find the product of 0.37 and 10.

     b. How is the product similar to 0.37? How is it different?

     c. Multiply the product from part (a) by 10. How is the product similar to 0.37? How is it different?

     d. In general, what do you think happens to a decimal number when you multiply it by 10?

46 Bits and Pieces III

STUDENT PAGE

Notes _____

_____

_____

_____

32. a. Give four different ways to label the unlabeled marks on the number line.

2.1

b. Find the mean of the five numbers in each of your answers in part (a). Do you see a pattern?

c. Can you label the unlabeled marks on the number line in part (a) so that the sum of the five numbers will be 10? Explain.

33. The area of a circle is 2.0096 square inches. Use 3.14 as an approximation for the number π.

a. What is the diameter of this circle?

b. What is the circumference of this circle?

Extensions

34. Leah filled her gas tank at the start of a trip and noted that her mileage indicator read 15,738.1 miles. When her mileage indicator read 16,167.6, she needed gas again. It took 18.2 gallons of gas to fill the tank. About how many miles did her car go on each gallon of gas?

35. Explore the decimal representations of fractions with a denominator of 99. Try $\frac{1}{99}, \frac{2}{99}, \frac{3}{99}$, and so on. What patterns do you see?

36. Explore the decimal representations of fractions with a denominator of 999. Try $\frac{1}{999}, \frac{2}{999}, \frac{3}{999}$, and so on. What patterns do you see?

Use the patterns you discovered in Exercises 35 and 36 to write fractions for these decimal representations.

37. 0.05050505 . . .   **38.** 0.45454545 . . .

39. 0.045045045 . . .   **40.** 10.121212 . . .

Notes _____

_____

_____

_____

Each of the shapes in Exercises 41–43 has the same area as the area of the rectangle.

1.2 cm

3.6 cm

Use this information to find the length marked by *n*.

41.

n

42.

n

2.88 cm

43.

3.84 cm

n

Notes _____

_____

_____

_____

Mathematical Reflections 3

In this investigation, you looked at the relationship between division of fractions and division of decimals. You also looked at patterns in decimal divisions that give the same answers. Finally, you looked at patterns in terminating and repeating decimal representations of fractions. The following questions will help you review and organize what you have learned.

Think about your answers to these questions. Discuss your ideas with other students and your teacher. Then write a summary of your findings in your notebook.

1. Describe a way to write a division problem that has the same answer as a given decimal division problem but has a whole number dividend and divisor. Use an example to help explain.

2. Describe an algorithm for dividing decimals. Tell why you think the algorithm works.

3. Explain how you can tell if a fraction has a terminating or a repeating decimal form.

Notes _____

_____

_____

_____

Investigation

ACE
Assignment Choices

Differentiated Instruction
Solutions for All Learners

Problem 3.1
Core 1–4, 28, 29
Other *Connections* 30

Problem 3.2
Core 5–14
Other *Connections* 31; unassigned choices from previous problems

Problem 3.3
Core 15–19, 22–24
Other *Applications* 20, 21; *Connections* 32–33; *Extensions* 34, 41–43; unassigned choices from previous problems

Problem 3.4
Core 27
Other *Applications* 25, 26; *Extensions* 35–40; unassigned choices from previous problems

Adapted For suggestions about adapting Exercises 1–4 and other ACE exercises, see the CMP *Special Needs Handbook*
Connecting to Prior Units 28, 32: *Bits and Pieces I;* 29: *Bits and Pieces II;* 33: *Covering and Surrounding*

Applications

1.–4. These are possible answers. Students may use other approaches. Check to be sure their explanations justify their choice of operation.

1. Subtraction; if you subtract the lower weight from the higher, you will find the difference between the two.

2. Division; you are finding how many $1\frac{1}{3}$ yards are in 6.5 yards.

3. Multiplication; you are adding the same value, $2.95, three times. This is equivalent to multiplying by 3.

4. Division; you are finding how many 0.26 meter lengths will fit into 42 meters or the total length of walkway that is being bricked.

5. Possible diagram and explanation: (Figure 1) $2.6 \div 0.4$ can be thought of as how many times does 0.4 go into 2.6. The diagram shows that there are 6 whole 0.4's in 2.6. There is a remainder of 0.2, which is half of the dividend 0.4. The solution means that there are $6\frac{1}{2}$ or 6.5 sets of 0.4 in 2.6.

6. a. Greater than 1; possible explanation: The divisor is less than the dividend, meaning it will go in more than once.

   b. Greater than 1; possible explanation: The divisor is less than the dividend, meaning it will go in more than once.

   c. Less than 1; possible explanation: The divisor is larger than the dividend. If you think of the problem as approximately $5 \div 11$, it can mean how many 11's fit into 5. Since 11 is greater than 5, it will not fit into 5 an entire time. About half of 11 will fit into 5.

   d. Less than 1; possible explanation: The divisor is larger than the dividend.

7. $\frac{45}{10} \div \frac{9}{10} = 45 \div 9 = 5$

8. $\frac{6}{10} \div \frac{12}{100} = \frac{60}{100} \div \frac{12}{100} = 60 \div 12 = 5$

9. $\frac{12}{10} \div \frac{5}{10} = 12 \div 5 = 2\frac{2}{5} = 2.4$

Figure 1

10. $\frac{18}{100} \div \frac{3}{100} = 18 \div 3 = 6$

11. $\frac{225}{10} \div \frac{15}{10} = 225 \div 15 = 15$

12. $\frac{342}{100} \div \frac{19}{100} = 342 \div 19 = 18$

13. $\frac{224}{10} \div \frac{5}{10} = 224 \div 5 = 44\frac{4}{5}$ or 44.8. The quotient means that five-tenths, or one-half, goes into 22.4 forty-four whole times and four-fifths of another whole more. If you had 22.4 feet of ribbon to make into bows that were 0.5 or $\frac{1}{2}$ ft in length, you would be able to make 44 complete bows and there would be enough ribbon left to make $\frac{4}{5}$, or 0.8, of another bow.

14. Possible answer: I can write $40.1 \div 0.5$ as $\frac{401}{10} \div \frac{5}{10}$. The answer to this fraction division problem is $401 \div 5$. So, the answer to the first problem is the same as the answer to the second.

15. 2.145

16. 361.04

17. 0.25

18. 0.199

19. a. 3   **b.** 0.3   **c.** 3

   d. 30   **e.** 0.03   **f.** 30

20. a. 3.875   **b.** 3.875   **c.** 3.875

   d. 3875   **e.** 0.3875   **f.** 3.875

21. a. 0.037

   b. It has the same digits, but they are in different decimal places. The seven, for example, is in the thousandths place.

   c. 0.0037. Again, it has the same digits but in different decimal places.

   d. In general, when dividing a number by 10, the digits stay the same, but the value of each digit shifts to the value of the next decimal place to the right.

22. a. Possible answer: $4.8 \div 1.2$; and $0.048 \div 0.012$. Each problem can be renamed as $48 \div 12$. For example, $0.048 \div 0.012$ is 48 thousandths divided by 12 thousandths. The size of the unit is thousandths, but the division problem is asking how many times does 12 thousandths go into 48 thousandths, or $48 \div 12$.

b. Possible answer: $480 \div 12$ and $48 \div 1.2$; each problem can be renamed as 480 thousandths $\div$ 12 thousandths.

23. N = 0.7; $0.42 \div 0.7 = 0.6, 0.42 \div 0.6 = 0.7$; $0.6 \times 0.7 = 0.42$; and $0.7 \times 0.6 = 0.42$

24. N = 3.2; $3.2 \div 0.5 = 6.4; 3.2 \div 6.4 = 3.2$; $6.4 \times 0.5 = 3.2; 0.5 \times 6.4 = 3.2$

25. a. 0.3333...   **b.** 0.3333...   **c.** 0.3333...

   d. Each of the three fractions, $\frac{2}{6}, \frac{13}{39}$, and $\frac{5}{15}$, are equivalent to the fraction $\frac{1}{3}$, whose decimal equivalent is 0.3333.... Any fraction that is equivalent to $\frac{1}{3}$ will have the decimal equivalent 0.3333....

26. a. 1.2222...   **b.** 1.2222...

   c. $\frac{11}{9}$ and $1\frac{6}{27}$ are equivalent to each other. They can both be expressed as $1\frac{2}{9}$ or the decimal equivalent 1.2222....

27. a.

Fraction	Decimal
$\frac{1}{9}$	0.111...
$\frac{2}{9}$	0.2222...
$\frac{3}{9}$	0.3333...
$\frac{4}{9}$	0.4444...
$\frac{5}{9}$	0.5555...
$\frac{6}{9}$	0.6666...
$\frac{7}{9}$	0.7777...
$\frac{8}{9}$	0.8888...

b. The numerator of the fraction repeats in the decimal, starting with the tenths place.

c. i. 1 (although the pattern suggests 0.999... in fact, the two answers are equal, $1 = 0.999...$)

   ii. 1.111...   **iii.** 1.666...

d. i. $1\frac{2}{9}$ **ii.** $2\frac{7}{9}$

Connections

28. a.

b.

c.

d.

e. Possible answer: I found the value of the middle mark, then found the middle of each of the lesser intervals.

29. D

30. a. Between 1968 and 1972, the score changed by 423.94 points.

b. Between 1976 and 1980, the score changed by 285.50 points.

c. Between 1996 and 2000, the score changed by 7.26 points.

d. 742.605 points

31. a. 3.7

b. The digits are the same, but they are in different decimal places. The seven, for example, is now in the tenths place instead of the hundredths place.

c. 37. Again, the digits are the same, but in different places.

d. In general, when we multiply a decimal number by 10, the digits will stay the same but will shift to the next decimal place to the left.

32. a. Possible answers:

b. The mean is always 2.1.

c. No. In order for the sum of the 5 positive numbers to be 10, their mean would have to be 2. This is not possible.

33. a. 1.6 in.; Since $A = \pi r^2$ we have so find r when $A = 2.0096$. Dividing 2.0096 by π, we get 0.64 for r^2 so $r = 0.8$. Thus the diameter is 2(0.8), or 1.6 in.

b. 5.024 in.; Since $C = \pi d$ we have that $C = \pi(1.6)$, or 5.024 in.

Extensions

34. About 23.6 miles per gallon; since in 429.5 miles she used 18.2 gallons of gas, dividing 429.4 by 18.2 we get about 23.6 miles per gallon.

35. $\frac{1}{99} = 0.010101\ldots$

$\frac{2}{99} = 0.020202\ldots$

$\frac{3}{99} = 0.030303\ldots$

$\frac{45}{99} = 0.454545\ldots$

In general, there is a repeating pattern of two digits. The numerator is the repeating number if it is greater than 10. If the numerator is less than 10, the repeating digits are 0 and the numerator.

36. $\frac{1}{999} = 0.001001001\ldots$

$\frac{2}{999} = 0.002002002\ldots$

$\frac{3}{999} = 0.003003003\ldots$

$\frac{45}{999} = 0.045045045\ldots$

$\frac{123}{999} = 0.123123123\ldots$

In general, there is a repeating pattern of three digits. The numerator is the repeating number if it is greater than 100. If the numerator is less than 100, the repeating digits are the numerator together with either one or two zeroes.

37. $\frac{5}{99}$ **38.** $\frac{45}{99}$ **39.** $\frac{45}{999}$ **40.** $10\frac{12}{99}$

41. 0.6 cm; the area of the original rectangle is $3.6 \times 1.2 = 4.32$ cm² so the area of this figure is also 4.32 cm². Since there are 12 squares, the area of each square must be 4.32 cm² ÷ 12 or 0.36 cm². Thus each square must be 0.6 cm on a side in order for the area to be 0.36 cm² since $0.6 \times 0.6 = 0.36$. Hence the length of n is 0.6 cm.

42. 1.5 cm; since the area of the parallelogram is $A = bh$ and $A = 4.32$ cm² and $b = 2.88$ cm, the height is 4.32 cm² ÷ 2.88 = 1.5 cm.

43. 2.25 cm; since the area of the triangle is $A = \frac{1}{2}bh$ with $A = 4.32$ cm² and $h = 3.84$ cm we get that $4.32 = \frac{1}{2}b(3.84)$. Using fractions we see that the equation is $\frac{432}{100} = \frac{50}{100} \times b \times \frac{384}{100}$ or $\frac{43,200}{10,000} = \frac{50}{100} \times b \times \frac{384}{100}$, so we need to find a number b such that $50 \times b \times 384$ is 43,200. If you divide 43,200 by 50 then this by 384 you get that b is 2.25 cm.

Possible Answers to Mathematical Reflections

1. Write the two decimal numbers as fractions. If the numbers are larger than 1, write improper fractions. Now, write these fractions with common denominators and whole-number numerators. The quotient of the numerators will be the same as the original quotient. For $0.4 \div 0.02$, we can write $\frac{4}{10} \div \frac{2}{100}$ and then $\frac{40}{100} \div \frac{2}{100} = 20$ because $40 \div 2$ is 20.

2. Rewrite the decimals as whole numbers, either by thinking about them as fractions as above, or by moving the decimal point in each number the same number of places, inserting zeros as necessary. As an example, $0.4 \div 0.02$ would require two moves of the decimal point for each number to become a whole number: $40 \div 2$.

Then divide by the usual whole number division algorithm. The quotient will be the same as the quotient of the original decimal numbers.

This algorithm works because the multiplication relationship (the *ratio*) between two numbers stays the same when they are multiplied by a common factor. In the example above, we are multiplying 0.4 and 0.02 each by 100 to obtain 40 and 2.

3. Fractions written in lowest terms with denominators that evenly divide a power of 10 will have terminating decimal representations. Examples include 4 (which divides 100 evenly), 5 (which divides 10), 8 (which divides 1,000 equally). In general, any fraction, which, in its lowest terms, has a denominator with a prime factorization including only 2's and/or 5's will have a terminating decimal representation.

Fractions written in lowest terms with denominators that do not evenly divide any power of 10 will have repeating decimal representations. Examples include 3 (which divides 9, but not 10; 99 but not 100; 999 but not 1,000, etc.), 7 (which divides itself but not 10, 98 but not 100, 994 but not 1000, and 9,996 but not 10,000, etc.) and 15. In general, any fraction, which, in its lowest terms, has a denominator with a prime factorization including any number other than 2 and/or 5 will have a repeating decimal representation.

Mathematical and Problem-Solving Goals

- Understand that a percent is a decimal fraction with a denominator of 100

- Represent $1.00 as 100 pennies, and relate this to partitioning a number line into 100 parts

- Represent percents as decimals and use decimal computation to compute percents

- Explore the relationship between 1% and 10% and use these to compute 5%, 15%, and 20% tips

- Work backwards to find the amount of the bill if you know the tip and the percent of tip for the bill

- Use percents in estimating or computing taxes, tips, and discounts

- Find what percent one number is of another number

- Solve problems using percents

Summary of Problems

Problem 4.1 Determining Tax

Problem 4.1 builds on the percent work in *Bits and Pieces I*. Sales tax is used to help students compute percents of numbers.

Problem 4.2 Computing Tips

Students compute tips and taxes on restaurant bills. Students use easy percents like 1% and 10% to compute 5%, 15%, and 20% tips.

Problem 4.3 Finding Bargains

Students compute discounts and taxes and find what percent one number is of another.

Overview

In *Bits and Pieces I*, we introduced students to the visual models of number lines and percent bars to describe percents. The notion of "Out of 100" and partitioning into a hundred equal-size lengths was used as a way of conceptualizing percent. The more readily your students can move among representations of fractions, decimals, and percents, the greater will be their "number sense" with percents.

This investigation uses percents with situations that involve money. Common settings for such situations include figuring out the amount of tax on a purchase, determining tips for meal service, and finding discounts on items. We encourage you to focus on two components: models such as number lines and percent bars to help students' thinking and the meaning of decimals as fractions with a denominator of 100.

Mathematics Background

For background on percent operations, see page 7.

	Suggested Pacing	Materials for Students	Materials for Teachers	ACE Assignments
All	$4\frac{1}{2}$ days	Calculators		
4.1	$1\frac{1}{2}$ days	Labsheet 4.1	Transparencies 4.1, 4.1A	1–3, 13, 14, 27–28
4.2	1 day	Labsheets 4.2A and 4.2B		4–7, 15–19, 29, 31–33
4.3	$1\frac{1}{2}$ days			8–12, 20–26, 30, 34–40
MR	$\frac{1}{2}$ day			

Goals

- Understand that a percent is a decimal fraction with a denominator of 100

- Represent $1.00 as 100 pennies, and relate this to partitioning a number line into 100 parts

- Represent percents as decimals and use decimal computation to compute percents

Problem 4.1 asks students to focus on the special role that "out of 100" plays when working with money. Students consider state sales tax on purchases. Some students are helped by thinking of a dollar as 100 pennies and relating this to a hundredths percent bar.

If you need to review percent bars, use the transparency master provided. You might use the problem, "What percent of the class is female if there are 35 students and 14 are girls?" This gives 40% girls and 60% boys. Then look at 34 students with 12 girls to discuss how you deal with approximations, since this is a little over 35% girls.

Launch 4.1

Students may want to use percent bars to work on this problem. Copies of Labsheet 4.1 should be available. Use the introduction to the problem with your class. This allows you to review percent bars and to make sure students understand the task. Ask them about the sales tax in your state and how it compares to the 6% sales tax.

Have students work in pairs.

Explore 4.1

As pairs work on the problem, encourage them to look for more than one way to solve the problem. Be sure they can explain their methods and why their ideas make sense. Ask questions about how Questions B and C of the problem are alike and different. How do these differences affect the answers?

If students are struggling, use a percent bar to help them think about the problem. If needed, you may want to stop and do a short summary of Question A and then have them continue with Question B. (See Figure 1.)

The answer is close to but less than 12.5 cents. The computation is $0.06 \times \$2 = \$0.12 = 12$ cents.

Summarize 4.1

When students have finished, have different pairs share their results and explain how they solved Question A.

The following conversation occurred in one classroom:

Classroom Dialogue Model

Teacher *What was the total cost of the CD Jill wants to buy when you include the sales tax, and how did you arrive at your amount? I need a group to share their ideas.*

Travis *It would cost $7.95 for the CD with tax. We got that by thinking that we have to pay 6 cents for each dollar we spend and the CD cost $7.50, so we added 6 cents seven times because there are seven dollars. Then we thought about the*

Figure 1

50 cents part of the cost, and since that is half a dollar we think you would need to pay half as much tax, so that would be 3 cents, so we added that on, and with the cost of the CD you add it all up, and you get $7.95.

Teacher *So you had a total of $7.95: $7.50 for the CD and 45 cents for the tax.*

Travis *Yes.*

Teacher *Comments or questions from anyone? Did anyone get something different or solve the problem a different way?*

Brandy *We sort of did what Travis and his partner did but different. We thought how $7.50 is 7 whole dollars and half of another dollar and for each dollar you have to pay 6 cents in taxes. So, we just multiplied 7 times 6 and got 42 cents and then added on another 3 cents for the half dollar and we ended up with 45 cents for tax and a total of $7.95 for the cost.*

Teacher *Comments or questions from anyone? Did anyone get something different or solve the problem a different way?*

Chris *We just multiplied $7.50 × 0.06 and got a tax of $0.45 for a total of $7.95.*

Marie *Wait, couldn't you just multiply $7.50 × 1.06 and get $7.95?*

Teacher *Why does that work?*

Marie *Well, we found that for $1.00 price and 6% sales tax, the price was 1.06. So you just multiply the price by the 1.06 to get cost.*

Teacher *Any other group want to share?*

Carl *We did this problem different than the other groups but got the same answer. We said that 6% means 6 out of 100 and rewrote it as the fraction $\frac{6}{100}$. Then we tried to write a fraction that would be equal to $\frac{6}{100}$ but have a denominator of 750. When we did that we got the new fraction to be $\frac{45}{750}$, and that means you have 45 cents for the tax and $7.95 for the total bill.*

Discuss the patterns that arise in Questions B and C when the percent is held constant for different quantities. Then look across parts B(1) and C(1), B(2) and C(2), B(3) and C(3), and describe what happens when the percent differs but the quantity stays the same. Look at how these patterns help one to think about finding percent of any number.

Suggested Question In each situation ask questions such as:

> • *If you pay 6% sales tax, what percent of the price do you pay?*

In the beginning, most students need to think of adding tax on problems in two stages. This question is meant to nudge them toward understanding that price + 6% of price = 100% plus 6% of price which is 106% of the price or 1.06 × price. It is fine if students continue to compute the tax and add it on, but the efficiency and understanding that come with realizing that you can do this in one step is worth working on over time.

Question D asks students to work backwards to find the price of the item when you know the percent of tax and the amount of the tax. Ask students to explain their strategies. Help them see that you can restate the question as "If 6% is $4.80, what is 100%?"

Visually on a percent bar the situation looks like this:

Students may focus on the part 6% is of 100% (or how many 6's in 100) and divide $\frac{100}{6}$ to get $16\frac{2}{3}$.

- *Now we know that we have to multiply 6% by 16⅔ to get 100%. What does that tell us about how to find the amount that goes on the percent bar under 100%?* (We need to multiply 16⅔ × \$4.80, which gives \$80.)

So, 16⅔ is the factor that we multiply 6% by to get 100% and \$4.80 by to get \$80. Let's put our work on the percent bar to remind us of our thinking.

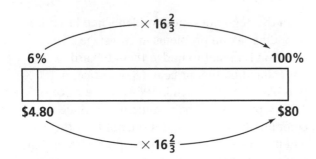

4.1 Determining Tax

Mathematical Goals

- Understand that a percent is a decimal fraction with a denominator of 100
- Represent $1.00 as 100 pennies, and relate this to partitioning a number line into 100 parts
- Represent percents as decimals and use decimal computation to compute percents

Launch

Students may want to use percent bars to work on this problem. Copies of Labsheet 4.1 should be available. Use the introduction to the problem with your class. This allows you to review percent bars and to make sure students understand the task. Ask them about the sales tax in your state and how it compares to the 6% sales tax. Have students work in pairs.

Materials
- Transparencies 4.1 and 4.1A
- Labsheet 4.1

Explore

As pairs work on the problem, encourage them to look for more than one way to solve the problem. Be sure they can explain their methods and why their ideas make sense. Ask questions about how Questions B and C of the problem are alike and different. How do these differences affect the answers?

If students are struggling, use a percent bar to help them think about the problem.

Summarize

Have different pairs share their results and explain how they solved Question A. Then look across parts B(1) and C(1), B(2) and C(2), B(3) and C(3), and describe what happens when the percent differs but the quantity stays the same. Look at how these patterns help one to think about finding the percent of any number. In each situation ask questions such as,

- *If you pay 6% sales tax, what percent of the price do you pay?*

This question is meant to nudge them toward understanding that price + 6% of price = 100% plus 6% of price, which is 106% of the price, or 1.06 × price. It is fine if students continue to compute the tax and add it on, but the efficiency and understanding that come with realizing that you can do this in one step is worth working on over time.

Question D asks students to work backwards to find the price of the item when you know the percent of tax and the amount of the tax. As students explain their strategies, help them see that you can restate the question as

Materials
- Student notebooks

continued on next page

"If 6% is $4.80, what is 100%?" Visually on a percent bar the situation looks like this:

Students may focus on the part 6% is of 100% (or how many 6's in 100) and divide $\frac{100}{6}$ to get $16\frac{2}{3}$.

- *Now we know that we have to multiply 6% by $16\frac{2}{3}$ to get 100%. What does that tell us about how to find the amount that goes on the percent bar under 100%?*

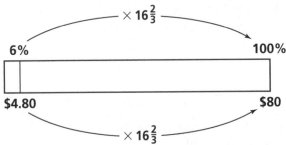

ACE Assignment Guide for Problem 4.1

Differentiated Instruction
Solutions for All Learners

Core 1–3, 13
Other *Connections* 14; *Extensions* 27, 28

Adapted For suggestions about adapting ACE exercises, see the CMP *Special Needs Handbook*.
Connecting to Prior Units 13–14: *Bits and Pieces I*

Answers to Problem 4.1

A. The total cost of the CD is $7.95. Tax is 45 cents. Students might have thought about it one of the ways described above or have thought 6 cents for every dollar and calculated 6 cents × 7.5, the number of dollars spent. 6 cents × 7.5 = 45 cents for tax, thus a total of $7.95.

B. 1. $2.12

   2. $5.30

   3. $0.53

C. 1. $2.14

   2. $5.35

   3. $0.53 or $0.54, depending on how the state rounds.

D. 1. Since for each dollar Alexis had to pay $0.06, you can find how many $0.06 are in $4.80. To answer this, compute 4.80 ÷ 0.06. This gives us $80 as the original cost. (The equation to solve is $p \times 0.06 = 4.80$.)

   2. Again we know that Frank paid $0.05 tax on each dollar. We can find how many dollars he paid tax on by finding how many groups of $0.05 are in the tax of $0.75. This gives us a cost of $15. (The equation to solve is $p \times 0.05 = 0.75$.)

4.2 Computing Tips

Goals

- Represent percents as decimals and use decimal computation to compute percents

- Explore the relationship between 1% and 10% and use these to compute 5%, 15%, and 20% tips

- Work backwards to find the amount of the bill if you know the tip and the percent of tip for the bill

This is a multi-step problem and will be a challenge for many students. However, it is a very important real-world use of percents. Students will benefit in their everyday use of mathematics as adults if we can help them understand percents and develop a facility in estimating or quickly computing taxes and tips. The problem involves determining tips for good service in a restaurant. Students are asked to consider the impact of including or not including state tax as part of the total price of food on which they determine tips and to look at the relationships between 5%, 10%, 15%, and 20% of an amount.

Launch 4.2

Talk with your students about going out to restaurants that have servers, people who come to your table, take your order, and bring your food to the table. Talk about the fact that it is customary in this country to leave a *tip* for service and that 15% to 20% of the bill is usually what is left.

Suggested Questions You might want to check to see if they understand the context by asking them the following:

- *If your food bill is $10 and you want to leave a 15% tip, how much is the tip?* ($1.50)

- *How does finding 10% help you find 15%?* (If you know 10%, 5% is half of that and you can add the amounts for 10% and 5% and get 15%.)

- *How does finding 10% help you find 20%?* (You can double the 10% to get 20%.)

- *If your bill is $12 and you want to leave a 15% tip, how much is the tip?* (10% is $1.20 and 5% is half, $0.60, so 15% is $1.80.)

- *How did you find the amount for the tip?* (By finding 10% in my head and using that to find 5%. Then 15% is the sum of 10% and 5%.)

- *If you wanted to leave a 20% tip, how much would the tip be?* ($2.40)

- *How did you find the amount for the tip?* (I doubled 10%.)

Be sure to discuss with your class whether the tip is different if they figured the tip before the sales tax had been added or after the tax had been added and what difference it would make.

Discuss the setting for Problem 4.2 with them. Groups of three or four work well for this problem. Groups will need a copy of Labsheets 4.2A and B. Remind them to fill out a lunch order to show what they planned to purchase and to show any computation that they do to answer the questions asked. Calculators should be available. Giving each group an order form on transparency to fill out for the group will speed up the summary.

Explore 4.2

As the students work in their small groups, encourage them to explore a variety of ways to solve this problem. Groups need to be sure that each person in their group can explain to the rest of the class their strategies for working on this problem. Students might want to use a calculator to determine the food bill and tax, since this is often already computed for them when their bill is presented. However, we seldom have a calculator with us in a restaurant, so we need to develop efficient ways to find or estimate the amount of tip that should be left.

If students have a hard time with Question B, have them compute 15% of an amount and then compute 5% and 10% of the amount and add. Comparing the results can help students see that these are the same. The basic building block for understanding what is going on with percents is noting that 1% of an amount can be multiplied by 15 to find 15%, etc.

INVESTIGATION 4

Summarize 4.2

One way to summarize this problem is to have groups of students move around the room to two or three other groups and see whether they agree with the written work of other groups. This gives everyone more practice and allows students to analyze the thinking of others.

Have a whole class discussion of the ways they worked on the problem. You might want to have a couple of groups share their order and how they found the total bill including tax, what size tip they left and how they found it, and how they determined how much each person needs to pay to share the bill equally.

Keep asking how the restaurant determines tax and how one can find the amount of tip to give. The parts of the problem should help to focus the summary on these two ideas. Here are some relationships that may help students:

- Ten percent of a number can be found by moving the decimal point since 10% of $1.00 is equal to $1 \times 0.10 = 0.10$, or $0.10. Using percent bars often helps students "see" this because they realize that to find 10%, you need to split the whole into 10 equal parts. Working with examples and looking for patterns helps students develop this connection with understanding.

0% 10%   100%

0   $.10 $1.00

- Recognizing that 5% is half of 10% helps you to get 15% easily. You can find 10% and then half of the 10% and add them together to get 15%. For example, if your restaurant bill is $14.90 plus the tax of 5%, the tax will be half of 10%. 10% is $1.49. Half of $1.49 is about $0.75. This makes the total bill $15.65. Now we need to estimate the tip. For a 15% tip we can estimate 10% and 5% and add the two. 10% of $15.65 is about $1.56. So, 5% is about $0.78. That makes the 15% tip $1.56 + $0.78, or $2.34.

- For 20% we can double the 10%. Using the example above, 10% is $1.56, double and you get $3.12.

This problem also raises the issue of how to round off amounts of tax and tip to usable amounts. If the bill for the meal is $19.45 and your state sales tax is 5%, students who multiply 19.45 by 0.05 will get 0.9725. How much money is $0.9725? A store might round up and call it $0.98 or down and call it $0.97. Dealing with numbers like this is confusing to some students. The problems with decimal amounts that are not nice comes up again when students have to share the total bill (food cost + tax + tip). In many cases the total bill (including tax and tip) does not give a number that can be evenly divided by 4 (or 3, depending on how many are in a group). Talk with students about how to interpret their quotient and how to round in sensible ways.

One idea that some teachers use after this problem is to offer extra credit if a student computes tip and tax outside school and brings in a note signed by an adult showing their work. This shows mathematics used in real situations and helps parents or guardians see an example of what students are learning in mathematics.

4.2 Computing Tips

Mathematical Goals

- Represent percents as decimals and use decimal computation to compute percents
- Explore the relationship between 1% and 10% and use these to compute 5%, 15%, and 20% tips
- Work backwards to find the amount of the bill if you know the tip and the percent of tip for the bill

Launch

Talk with your students about going out to restaurants and that it is customary in this country to leave a *tip* for service and that 15% to 20% of the bill is usually what is left. You might want to check to see if they understand the context by asking them the following:

- *If your food bill is $10 and you want to leave a 15% tip, how much is the tip?*
- *How does finding 10% help you find 15%?*
- *How does finding 10% help you find 20%?*
- *If your bill is $12 and you want to leave a 15% tip, how much is the tip?*
- *How did you find the amount for the tip?*

Be sure to discuss whether the tip is different if they figured it before the sales tax had been added or after the tax had been added and what difference it would make.

Discuss the setting for Problem 4.2. Have students work in groups of three or four. Groups should fill out the lunch order to show what they planned to purchase and to show any computation that they do to answer the questions asked. Calculators should be available. You may wish to give each group an order form on transparency to fill out for the summary.

Materials

- Labsheets 4.2A and 4.2B
- Transparency of Labsheet 4.2B (optional)

Explore

As the students work, encourage them to explore a variety of ways to solve this problem. Students might want to use a calculator to determine the food bill and tax, since this is often already computed for them when their bill is presented. However, we seldom have a calculator with us in a restaurant, so we need to develop efficient ways to find or estimate the amount of tip that should be left.

If students have a hard time with Question B, have them compute 15% of an amount and then compute 5% and 10% of the amount and add. The basic building block for understanding what is going on with percents is noting that 1% of an amount can be multiplied by 15 to find 15%, etc.

continued on next page

Have groups share their order and how they found the total bill including tax, what size tip they left and how they found it, and how they determined how much each person needs to pay to share the bill equally. Keep asking how the restaurant determines tax and how one can find the amount of tip to give.

Materials
- Student notebooks

ACE Assignment Guide for Problem 4.2

Core 4–6, 31, 32
Other *Applications* 7; *Connections* 15–19; *Extensions* 29, 33; unassigned choices from previous problems

Adapted For suggestions about adapting Exercise 6 and other ACE exercises, see the CMP *Special Needs Handbook*.
Connecting to Prior Units 17–19: *Bits and Pieces I*

Answers to Problem 4.2

A. Answers will vary depending on what is ordered and what amount of tip is left.

B. 1. 10% is $2, 5% is $1. Note, 5% is half as much as 10%.

2. 10% is $2.45, 20% is $4.90. Note, 20% is twice as much as 10%.

3. 10% is $1.73 or $1.74. 15% is the same as 10% plus 5% and 5% is half of 10%, so 15% is $1.74 + $.87 (half of 10%) = $2.61.

20% is twice as much as 10%, so $1.74 + $1.74 (or $1.73 + $1.73) = $3.48 (or $3.46).

C. 1. Her method works because the tax is 5% of the food. 15% is 3 times 5%.

2. 20% is 4 groups of 5% so multiplying the tax by 4 would give you 20%. $0.38 × 4 = $1.52.

D. 1. $1.55 since 4 × $0.38 would be $1.52 and rounded up to the nearest multiple of 5 cents would make it $1.55.

2. A meal price between $4.51 and $5.00, but no higher, may be given.

3. A meal price between $29.34 and $30.00, but no higher, may be given.

4. $12.50

4.3 Finding Bargains

Goals

- Use percents in estimating or computing taxes, tips, and discounts
- Find what percent one number is of another number
- Solve problems using percents

Discounts and sales are common situations that individuals deal with daily. Problem 4.3 involves considering what it means to get a certain percent discount on items being sold. Finding what percent discount a coupon with a dollar value will give on the price of the item you want to purchase raises the issue of finding what percent one number is of another.

Launch 4.3

Calculators should be available for students. Have a conversation with your students about what it means when a store offers a sale or discount on items.

Suggested Questions Ask:

- *What does it mean when a store has a Saturday Special Sale and everything in the store is 25% off?* (You will get 25 cents off each dollar of the price of items you buy.)

- *If everything is 25% off, what percent of the price do you have to pay?* (It means that you will pay only 75% of the marked price of any item in the store.)

- *If something costs $10 and there is a 25% off sale, how much do you have to pay for this item?* ($7.50) *How much do you save?* ($2.50)

- *If something is $50 and there is a 25% off sale, how much do you have to pay for this item?* ($37.50) *How much do you save?* ($12.50)

- *How did you find those amounts?* (Take 75% of the costs to find what you pay and 25% of the cost for what you save. You also can subtract the 75% from the price to get the savings.)

Be sure students understand what Problem 4.3 is asking them to do. Some students find multi-step problems difficult. You might want to assign Question A and then discuss it with the class before they proceed to work on Questions B, C, and D.

Have them work with a partner to answer the questions. Encourage pairs to explore a variety of ways to solve this problem.

Explore 4.3

Remind them that they will need to explain their strategies to the rest of the class. Help students see how percent bars can be used to represent the problem.

Watch for the following misconception. In Question B, some students think that 10% off one CD single means that if you buy 3 CD singles, you will get 30% off.

Suggested Question If you see this misconception, you might ask,

- *If you buy 10 CD singles, what percent off would the store give you by your method?* (100% off) *Is that reasonable?* (No.)

This should cause students to rethink.

Another question students ask is whether 10% off the whole is the same as 10% off each CD single. Here you can help students understand by asking them to compute each way and compare the answers. For students who understand that taking 90% of the cost is the same as subtracting 10% of the cost from the cost, they might write: $3(3.45) \times 0.90$ and $0.90(3.45) + 0.90(3.45) + 0.90(3.45)$ and compare.

Others will write: $3(3.45) - 0.10 \times 3(3.45)$ and $(3.45 - 0.10 \times 3.45) + (3.45 - 0.10 \times 3.45) + (3.45 - 0.10 \times 3.45)$ and compare. This may be a chance to introduce the Distributive Property. While we do not formally define this property until grade seven, if the opportunity arises and the students are interested and ready, go ahead and help them think about the fact that we could just multiply by three rather than add the three terms that are exactly the same.

Have a whole class discussion of the ways students found to solve each of the problems. Ask students to explain their strategies and to tell why they are reasonable. If you have assigned Question A and discussed it before students proceed, this allows for some in-class practice with these ideas in a supportive manner. Question D can serve as a summary for the discussions that have taken place in this unit up to this point. After this discussion, some individual work from the ACE section would give students another opportunity to practice solving these types of problems.

Be sure to end the summary by pulling together different strategies for thinking about percents. Several strategies are possible. Below are a couple of examples from different classes.

Example 1: Meaning of Percents

To find the percent of a number, I think about percent as meaning "so much of 100." So if I want to find 5%, that means I need 5 out of every 100. If I have a number that is not a multiple of 100, then I think how the number compares to 100. For example, if I need to find 5% of 250, 250 is 2 and a half groups of 100. So I need 2 and a half groups of 5 if I am trying to find 5%. That would be

$$5 + 5 + 2\tfrac{1}{2} = 12\tfrac{1}{2}.$$

Example 2: 1% Method

For any number, you can find 1% of it by moving the decimal to the left two places (or divide by 100) because 1% means $\frac{1}{100}$th. Then, once you have found 1% of a number, you can find any other percent just by multiplying. If you want to find 7% of 250 then you first find 1% of 250, which is 2.5, and then you multiply by 7 because 7% is seven 1%'s. You get 17.5. So 7% of 250 is 17.5.

4.3 Finding Bargains

Mathematical Goals

- Use percents in estimating or computing taxes, tips, and discounts
- Find what percent one number is of another number
- Solve problems using percents

Launch

Calculators should be available for students. Have a conversation with your students about what it means when a store offers a sale or a discount on items.

- *What does it mean when a store has a Saturday Special Sale and everything in the store is 25% off?*
- *If everything is 25% off, what percent of the price do you have to pay?*
- *If something costs $10 and there is a 25% off sale, how much do you have to pay for this item? How much do you save?*
- *If something is $50 and there is a 25% off sale, how much do you have to pay for this item? How much do you save?*
- *How did you find those amounts?*
- *What percent of the original price do you pay?*

Be sure students understand what Problem 4.3 is asking them to do. Some students find multi-step problems difficult. You might want to assign Question A and then discuss it with the class before they proceed to work on Questions B, C, and D. Have them work with a partner to answer the questions.

Explore

Remind them that they will need to explain their strategies to the rest of the class. Help students see how percent bars can be used to represent the problem.

Watch for the following misconception. In Question B, some students may think that 10% off one CD single means that if you buy three CD singles, you will get 30% off. If you see this misconception, you might ask,

- *If you buy 10 CD singles, what percent off would the store give you by your method? Is that reasonable?*

This should cause students to rethink.

Another question students ask is whether 10% off the whole is the same as 10% off each CD single. Here you can help students understand by asking them to compute each way and compare the answers.

Summarize

Ask students to explain their strategies and to tell why they are reasonable.

If you have assigned Question A and discussed it before students proceed, this allows for some in-class practice with these ideas in a supportive manner. The ideas in these problems are difficult for some students because of the multiple steps needed to actually arrive at a solution. Question D can serve as a summary for the discussions that have taken place in this unit up to this point.

Be sure to end the summary with pulling together different strategies for thinking about percents. See the extended Summarize for discussion of strategies.

ACE Assignment Guide for Problem 4.3

Core 8–12, 20–22, 35–39
Other *Connections* 23–26; *Extensions* 30, 34, 40; unassigned choices from previous problems

Adapted For suggestions about ACE exercises, see the CMP *Special Needs Handbook*.
Connecting to Prior Units 20–26: *Bits and Pieces I*

Answers to Problem 4.3

A. $16.53
$15.95 + $3.45 = $19.40
$19.40 – 2($1.94) = $19.40 – $3.88 = 15.52
$15.52 × 6.5% = $1.0088, which gets rounded to $1.01. (Some stores charge tax on the original price!) $15.52 + $1.01 = $16.53 needed.

B. Jeremy is correct. Six singles will cost $20.70 before the discount and $16.56 after the discount. The 6.5% tax on $16.56 is $1.08. The total cost is $17.64. This is less than the $18.59 for a CD and CD single.

C. 1. $47.85;
   15 × $15.95 = $239.25
   $239.25 × 20% = $47.85, the amount of discount.

   2. $239.25 × 0.01 = $2.3925 (rounded to $2.39 or $2.40)

3. 20% of the cost ($47.85) is 20 times 1% of the cost (2.3925). If you round 2.3925 to 2.39, then the amounts 2.39 × 20 are slightly different due to rounding error.

4. Once you have the amount for a 1% discount, you can multiply that amount by 16 to get a 16% discount; you can multiply 16% (0.16) times the cost to get the discount; these are related because 1% × 16 = 16%.

D. 1. 25% discount. You could reason that 12 is $\frac{1}{4}$ of 48 to get the 25% discount.

2. You can see that there are five $25 amounts in $125. So the percent off is equal to $\frac{1}{5}$, or 20%. You can also divide 25 by 125 to get 0.2 or 20%.

3. Answers will vary. Possible answer: To find what percent a number a is of a number b, you can find what part of number b the number a represents. How many a's are needed to make b? Use this to write a fraction, which we can then write as a percent.

For example: 15 is what percent of 75? 75 ÷ 15 = 5. That is, there are five 15's in 75. So 15 is $\frac{1}{5}$, or 20%, of 75.

The student edition pages for this
investigation begin on the next page.

Notes _____

_____

_____

_____

Investigation 4

Using Percents

When a store has a sale, you see advertisements for discounts. The discounts are usually given in percents (20% off, 30% off, etc.). Percents are helpful in many situations involving money. Discounts, taxes, and tips are all described with percents. Understanding how to compute and use these percents can make you a smarter consumer.

4.1 Determining Tax

Remember that a percent is a special way of representing a fraction (or rate) with a denominator of 100. You can think of percent as meaning "out of 100."

Most states have a sales tax. A sales tax of 6% means that for every dollar an item costs, a person needs to pay an additional six hundredths of a dollar, which is 6 cents, or $0.06, for taxes:

$$\$1.00 + (6\% \text{ of } \$1.00) = \$1.00 + \$0.06 = \$1.06$$

Or, since $1.00 is 100 pennies:

$$100 \text{ pennies} + (6\% \text{ of } 100 \text{ pennies}) = 100 \text{ pennies} + 6 \text{ pennies}$$
$$= 106 \text{ pennies}$$
$$= \$1.06$$

You can use this same type of reasoning with other sales tax problems.

Notes _____

_____

_____

_____

States, and sometimes counties and cities, establish sales tax for certain goods and services. Some states have a higher sales tax than others.

- What is the sales tax in your area?
- How does it compare to the taxes in other parts of the country?

Problem 4.1 Determining Tax

A. Jill wants to buy a CD that is priced at $7.50. The sales tax is 6%. What will be the total cost of the CD? Try to find more than one way to solve this problem. Be prepared to explain the different methods you find.

B. Using a sales tax of 6%, find the total cost for each item.

    1. a $2.00 magazine   **2.** a $5.00 book on dogs

    3. a $0.50 comic book

C. Use a sales tax of 7%. Find the total cost for each item in Question B.

D. Use what you have learned to solve these problems.

    1. Alexis bought a CD player. She does not remember the price, but she does know that the 6% sales tax came to $4.80. What was the price of the CD player? Explain your reasoning.

    2. Frank buys a new video game. The 5% sales tax is $0.75. What is the price of the game? Explain.

ACE **Homework starts on page 55.**

Connected Mathematics

SALE $7.50

The Soundtrack

4.2 Computing Tips

You have developed some strategies for computing a sales tax and finding the total cost. As you work on Problem 4.2, look for more shortcuts and strategies for solving problems involving taxes and tips.

At most restaurants, customers pay their server a tip for providing good service. A typical tip is 15% to 20% of the price of the meal. Some people calculate the tip based on the price of the meal before the tax is added. Others base the tip on the total cost after the tax is added.

Investigation 4 Using Percents   **51**

STUDENT PAGE

Notes _____

_____

_____

_____

Try to find more than one way to solve the problems. Be prepared to explain the different methods you used.

A. Have each member of your group use the menu shown to make up a lunch order. Write a list of all the items ordered by your group.

Larry's Lunch Place

Lunch Specials

Roast Turkey..................................3.95
Slices of turkey breast, savory dressing, homemade gravy, and cranberry sauce

Veggie Quesadilla 3.95
Whole-wheat tortillas stuffed with tomatoes, roasted peppers, and three kinds of cheese

Chicken Tenders 4.50
Strips of all-white-meat chicken baked to a golden brown, served with a baked potato, coleslaw, and barbeque sauce

Baked Meatloaf............................3.95
Tasty homestyle meatloaf with mixed green salad

Spaghetti with Tomato Sauce......3.25
A generous portion of pasta with zesty sauce, parmesan cheese, and garlic bread

Grilled Chicken Breast..................5.25
Served over rice with lemon parsley sauce, crisp lettuce, tomato slices, and whole wheat rolls (low cholesterol)

Larry's Famous Burgers

**Quarter Pound
Hamburger Platter**......................3.30

**Quarter Pound
Cheeseburger Platter**...................3.60

Larry's Special...............................4.35
Two patties, with crisp lettuce, Larry's own sauce, and cheese on a specially baked bun

Seafood

Shrimp Cocktail 6.95
Tender steamed shrimp served on ice with tangy cocktail sauce

Fish and Chips 4.45
Three deep-fried fillets with french fries, coleslaw, and tartar sauce

Desserts

Fresh Strawberry Pie...................1.89
With frozen yogurt................................2.25
Chocolate Cake 1.50
With ice cream 1.95

Beverages

Coffee, Regular or Decaffeinated .... .80
Hot or Iced Tea.....................................80
White or Chocolate Milk.....................99
Lemonade...99
Soft Drinks..99
Orange Juice 99
Hot Chocolate 99
Root Beer Float 1.99

Notes _____

_____

_____

_____

1. Find the total bill for food and tax for your group. Use a sales tax of 6%.

2. How much will you leave for the tip? (The tip must be between 15% and 20%.)

3. Your group members decide to share the cost of the meal equally. What is each person's share of the cost, including the tip?

B. Many people use benchmarks for determining tips. Gil explains his strategy: "I always figure out 10% of the bill, and then I use this information to calculate a 15% or 20% tip."

1. Find 10% and 5% of $20.00. How are the two percents related?

2. Find 10% and 20% of $24.50. How are the two percents related?

3. Find 10% of $17.35. Use this to find 15% and 20% of $17.35. Explain.

C. The sales tax in Kadisha's state is 5%. Kadisha says she computes a 15% tip by multiplying the tax shown on her bill by three. For a bill with a tax charge of $0.38, Kadisha's tip is $0.38 × 3 = $1.14.

Garden Cafe	
ITEM	AMOUNT
Food	$7.55
5% Tax	.38
TOTAL	$7.93

1. Why does Kadisha's method work?

2. Use a similar method to compute a 20% tip. Explain.

D. When people leave a 15% or 20% tip, they often round up to the nearest multiple of 5 or 10 cents. For example, in Question C, Kadisha might leave a tip of $1.15 rather than $1.14.

1. If Kadisha always rounds up, what is a 20% tip on her bill?

2. Omar always leaves a 20% tip based on the meal price before tax is added. Find a meal price for which Omar leaves a tip of $1.00 after rounding up to the nearest multiple of 5 or 10 cents.

3. Marlene always leaves a 15% tip based on the meal price before tax. Find a meal price for which Marlene leaves a tip of $4.50 after rounding up to the nearest multiple of 5 or 10 cents.

4. Customers leave Jerome $2.50 as a tip for service. The tip is 20% of the total bill for their food. How much is the bill?

ACE Homework starts on page 55.

Notes _____

_____

_____

_____

4.3 Finding Bargains

At Loud Sounds Music, CDs are regularly priced at $15.95, and CD singles are regularly priced at $3.45. Every day this month, the store is offering a discount on all CDs and CD singles.

Problem 4.3 Using Discounts

Jeremy goes to Loud Sounds. He discovers that if he buys two or more items today, he can save 20% on each item.

A. Suppose Jeremy buys a CD and a CD single. The store adds a 6.5% sales tax on the discounted price. How much does Jeremy spend?

B. Jeremy thinks he can buy six CD singles for less money than the cost of one CD single and a CD. Is he correct? Explain your reasoning.

C. Mr. Fernandes wants to take advantage of the day's 20% special to add to his CD collection. There are 15 CDs he wants to buy.

   1. What is the total amount of the discount he will receive?

   2. Suppose the discount is only 1%. What total discount amount would Mr. Fernandes receive on the 15 CDs?

   3. What is the relationship between 1% and 20% of the cost?

   4. How can you use what you found out above to find a 16% discount on the cost of the 15 CDs? Can you find another way to compute 16%? Explain your methods and how they are related.

D. 1. At another music store, Rita gets a $12 discount off a purchase of $48. What percent discount does she get?

   2. Masako has a $25-off coupon on a purchase of $100 or more at a department store. She buys a jacket with a price tag of $125. What percent off does she get on her purchase?

   3. Describe how you answered parts (1)–(2). Explain why your method works.

ACE Homework starts on page 55.

Notes _____

_____

_____

_____

Applications

1. Find three examples of percents used in the real world. Newspapers, magazines, radio, and television are good places to look. Write down each example, or cut it out and tape it to your paper. For each example, describe how percents are used and what they mean.

2. Hot dogs at a carnival cost $0.99 each plus 7% tax. What is the total cost for one hot dog?

3. Jason stops at a ball-toss game at the carnival. The sign reads, "Three balls for 50 cents or six balls for 80 cents." What percent does he save by buying one set of six balls instead of two sets of three balls?

4. A class conducts a survey of 1,000 students.

   a. The survey reveals that 20% of the students speak Spanish. How many students is this?

   b. 6% of the students have forgotten their locker combinations at some time. How many students is this?

   c. Of the sixth-grade students surveyed, 12% bring their lunches to school. Suppose 24 sixth-graders do this. How many sixth-graders are at the school?

5. a. Arif and Keisha go to a restaurant for dinner. Their meals total $13.75. The sales tax is 5%. How much tax is added to the bill?

   b. They want to leave a 15% tip based on the bill and the tax combined. How much should they leave? Explain.

   c. Arif ordered a more expensive meal than Keisha. After tax and tip are figured, he decides he should pay $3 more than Keisha. How much should each pay?

Notes
_____
_____
_____
_____

6. Jen and Sarah go to lunch at the Green Grill. Their meal totals $28. The sales tax is 6%.

Go Online
PHSchool.com
For: Multiple-Choice Skills
Practice
Web Code: ama-6454

  a. What is the total cost with the tax?

  b. They want to leave a 20% tip based on the total cost before the tax. How much tip should they leave?

  c. Describe two strategies that Jen and Sarah can use to figure the amount of the tip.

7. Marilyn carries a tip calculator card with her. It lists the amounts for 15% and 20% tips on whole dollar values up to $100. Her daughter notices a pattern. She says, "For each dollar the cost increases, the tips in the 15% column increase $0.15."

  a. Explain why this pattern occurs for 15% tip values.

  b. What is the amount of increase for each dollar increase in the 20% tip column?

  c. The tip calculator card only goes up to $100. How can you use the card if your restaurant bill totals $325?

8. The Science Supply Store is having a sale. All graduated cylinders are 25% off. Mrs. Delmar buys four graduated cylinders that were originally $8 each and six that were originally $9.50 each.

  a. How much money will Mrs. Delmar save?

  b. What percent of the original price will Mrs. Delmar pay?

  c. Suppose the sales tax is 4%. What is Mrs. Delmar's total cost?

The local boutique is having a sale on hats. All regular-priced hats are 20% off. Shirley, Lisa, and Sandy each find a hat to buy.

9. Shirley's beach hat was originally $24.95. What is the sale price?

10. Sandy finds a sun visor that was originally $12.50. What is the sale price?

11. Lisa finds a hat that is already marked down. The price tag shows that the original price was $36. The marked-down price is $27. What percent has the hat been marked down? Explain.

Notes _____

_____

_____

_____

12. **a.** Inline skates are on sale for 35% off the regular price. What fraction off is this discount?

    b. The original price of one pair of inline skates is $124.99. What is the sale price?

    c. A tax of 5% is computed on the sale price. What is the total cost of the inline skates?

Connections

13. Theo does $\frac{3}{10}$ of his homework. What percent is equal to $\frac{3}{10}$? What percent does Theo still have left to do?

14. **Multiple Choice** In a survey, 75% of 400 parents said they give their children fruit as a snack. How many parents of those surveyed is this?

    A. 150   **B.** 200   **C.** 225   **D.** 300

15. If $2.4 \div 0.2 = 12$, is $2.4 \div 0.5$ greater than or less than 12? Explain.

16. If $0.25 \times 0.8 = 0.2$, is $0.25 \div 0.8$ greater than or less than 0.2?

17. A certain bean plant grows 15% of its height each day. Express this percent as a decimal.

18. **Multiple Choice** Ike's Bikes requires 25% of the cost as a down payment for a new mountain bike. What fraction of the cost is this percent?

    F. $\frac{9}{35}$ **G.** $\frac{5}{21}$ **H.** $\frac{8}{32}$ **J.** $\frac{7}{24}$

Homework
Help Online
PHSchool.com
For: Help with Exercise 15
Web Code: ame-6415

Notes _____

_____

_____

_____

19. Four friends order a square pizza. Marisa says she isn't very hungry and only wants 10% of the pizza. Tomarr is very hungry and says he will eat 50% of the pizza. Jon says he will eat 35%, and Kwan says she will eat 15%. Is this possible? Explain your reasoning.

20. The Running Shoe Company advertises that they will award prizes for 1% of the total number of entries in a contest. They receive 1,600 entries. How many prizes do they award?

In Exercises 21 and 22, a paint spill covers up part of the fraction strips. Use what is showing to reason about each set of strips and to find fractions equivalent to those marked.

21.

22.

Find numbers that will make each sentence true. There may be more than one solution. If so, show at least two solutions.

23. $\frac{4}{9} = \frac{\blacksquare}{\blacksquare}$ **24.** $\frac{\blacksquare}{\blacksquare} = \frac{3}{5}$ **25.** $\frac{\blacksquare}{3} = \frac{8}{\blacksquare}$ **26.** $\frac{5}{\blacksquare} = \frac{\blacksquare}{18}$

Notes _____

_____

_____

_____

Extensions

27. Write a percent problem that involves discounts on food, cars, books, clothes, or other items. Solve your problem.

28. You are shopping in Chicago, Illinois, where the state sales tax is $6\frac{1}{4}\%$. You purchase a $5.00 map of the city. What is your total cost?

29. Carrie buys a pair of jeans that cost $32.00. The local sales tax is $2\frac{1}{2}\%$ and the state sales tax is 5%.

Now Only $32.00

   a. What is the amount of each tax?

   b. What is the total cost of the jeans?

30. In January the news reported an inflation rate of 4%. In February, the news reported that inflation had increased by 10% since the January report. What does that mean? What is the new rate of inflation?

For Exercises 31 and 32, copy the number line (including all the labeled marks). Mark each number line at 1. Rewrite each fraction, including 1, as a decimal and a percent.

31.

   0         $\frac{3}{4}$

32.

   0               $\frac{5}{3}$

33. Copy the percent bar below. Mark it carefully to show the location of 100%.

0%   120%

Notes _____

_____

_____

_____

34. Each year the Mannel Department Store has a big end-of-summer sale. At the sale, they give customers an additional 25% off on all marked-down merchandise.

a. A beach towel had an original price of $22. It was marked down 10%. What is the final price, after the additional 25% discount?

b. A patio table and four chairs originally cost $350. They were marked down 50%. What is the final cost of the table and chairs with the additional discount?

Find numbers that will make each sentence true.

35. $\frac{1}{3} = \frac{\blacksquare}{9} = \frac{\blacksquare}{6}$ **36.** $\frac{\blacksquare}{18} = \frac{8}{12} = \frac{4}{\blacksquare}$ **37.** $\frac{3}{\blacksquare} = \frac{12}{\blacksquare} = \frac{9}{\blacksquare}$ **38.** $\frac{\blacksquare}{3} = \frac{\blacksquare}{21} = \frac{\blacksquare}{6}$

39. In Exercises 35–38, which sentences have more than one possible answer? Why?

40. A box of macaroni and cheese says that it makes 25% more than the regular box. If a regular box makes three cups of macaroni and cheese, how many cups will this box make?

Notes _____

_____

_____

_____

Mathematical Reflections 4

In this investigation you solved problems that involved finding percents of numbers. You computed discounts, sale prices, tips, and sales tax. The following questions will help you summarize what you have learned.

Think about your answers to these questions. Discuss your ideas with other students and your teacher. Then write a summary of your findings in your notebook.

1. Explain how to find the sales tax on a purchase and calculate the final bill. Use an example.

2. Describe a procedure for finding the price of a discounted item if you know the percent of the discount.

3. **a.** Explain a process for finding 17% of a number if you know 1% and 5% of the number.

   b. Give five other percents of a number that are easy to find if you know 1% and 5% of the number.

4. Describe how to find the cost of a purchase if you know the percent of the tax and the amount of the sales tax on the purchase.

5. How can you find the percent one number is of another? For example, what percent of 35 is 7?

Notes _____

_____

_____

_____

Investigation

ACE
Assignment Choices

Differentiated Instruction
Solutions for All Learners

Problem 4.1
Core 1–3, 13
Other *Connections* 14; *Extensions* 27, 28

Problem 4.2
Core 4–6, 31, 32
Other *Applications* 7; *Connections* 15–19;
Extensions 29, 33; unassigned choices from
previous problems

Problem 4.3
Core 8–12, 20–22, 35–39
Other *Connections* 23–26; *Extensions* 30, 34, 40;
unassigned choices from previous problems

Adapted For suggestions about adapting
Exercise 6 and other ACE exercises, see the
CMP *Special Needs Handbook*.
Connecting to Prior Units 13–14, 17–26: *Bits and Pieces I*

Applications

1. Answers will vary.

2. $1.06; 0.99(1.07) = 1.0593.

3. 20%; the cost for 3 balls is 50 cents, so at the
same rate, 6 balls should cost $1. Since the
cost for 6 balls is 80 cents (which is 20 cents
less than the $1) and 20 cents is 20% of $1,
Jason is saving 20%.

4. **a.** 200 students speak Spanish.
   b. 60 students have forgotten their locker
   combinations.
   c. 200 sixth graders; since 12% is 24 students,
   1% would be 2 students. To find 100%,
   multiply the number of students for 1%, 2,
   by 100 to get 200 students.

5. **a.** $0.69 is added for tax.
   b. The two should leave approximately $2.17.
   c. Arif should pay $9.81, and Keisha should
   pay $6.80. This totals $16.61, which is also
   the sum of the food, tax, and tip. Note: A
   common student error is to find half of the
   bill and add $3.00 for Arif's share. Doing so
   will result in Arif paying $6.00 more than
   Keisha. Instead, Arif should pay $1.50 more
   than half the total.

6. **a.** $29.68
   b. $5.60
   c. One strategy is to find 10% ($2.80), then
   double this amount. Another strategy is to
   divide the whole bill (100%) by 5 to get
   20% of the bill.

7. **a.** This pattern reflects the meaning of 15%
   tax. 15 cents is added for every dollar since
   15 cents is 15% of a dollar.
   b. There would be a 20 cent increase in the tip
   column for each dollar in the bill column.
   c. One strategy is to multiply the tip for $100
   by 3.25. Another strategy is to multiply the
   tip for $100 by 3, then to add the tip for $25.

8. **a.** Her total before the discount would be $89.
   She saved 25% of this, or $22.25.
   b. 75%
   c. $69.42

9. $19.96

10. $10.00

11. 25%. $9.00 has been taken off the price. 9 is
    one-fourth of 36, because the hat is 25% off.

12. **a.** $\frac{35}{100}$ or $\frac{7}{20}$
    b. $81.25
    c. $85.31

Connections

13. He has done 30%. He still needs to do 70%.

14. D

15. The answer will be less than 12. In the second problem, you are dividing by a larger number, thus it will have a smaller quotient.

16. The answer will be greater. One way to see this is to realize that dividing by 0.8 ($\frac{8}{10}$) is the same as multiplying by $\frac{10}{8}$. Now you are multiplying by a larger number than in the first problem, resulting in a larger product.

17. 0.15   **18.** H

19. This will not be possible because the percents add to more than 100%. This is more than the amount of pizza they have.

20. 16 prizes

21. $\frac{6}{9}$ **22.** $\frac{3}{9} = \frac{6}{18}$

23. Possible answers: $\frac{8}{18}, \frac{12}{27}$

24. Possible answers: $\frac{6}{10}, \frac{9}{15}$

25. Possible answers:
$\frac{1}{3} = \frac{8}{24}, \frac{2}{3} = \frac{8}{12}, \frac{4}{3} = \frac{8}{6}, \frac{8}{3} = \frac{8}{3}, \frac{24}{3} = \frac{8}{1}$

26. Possible answers: $\frac{5}{9} = \frac{10}{18}, \frac{5}{3} = \frac{30}{18}$

Extensions

27. Answers will vary.

28. $5.31

29. a. Local tax is $0.80. State tax is $1.60.

   b. $34.40

30. New inflation rate will be 4.4%. 4% inflation means something that costs a dollar now will cost 4 cents more one year from now. If inflation increases 10%, this means that this increase will be 10% larger or 4.4 cents per dollar. A common mistake is to add 4% and 10% and say 14% as the answer. However, if we wish to say that inflation increased to 14% from 4%, we need to say that it increased 10 *percent points*, or that inflation increased 250%.

This makes sense if you think about what it would mean for inflation to double from 4%. This would mean a 100% increase in inflation to 8%.

31.

32.

33.

34. a. $14.85 (Note: Some students may want to take 35% of $22. This is incorrect. It requires two procedures: 10% off $22 and then 25% off $19.80.)

   b. $131.25

35. $\frac{1}{3} = \frac{3}{9} = \frac{2}{6}$

36. $\frac{12}{18} = \frac{8}{12} = \frac{4}{6}$

37. One possible answer: $\frac{3}{2} = \frac{12}{8} = \frac{9}{6}$

38. One possible answer: $\frac{1}{3} = \frac{7}{21} = \frac{2}{6}$

39. Exercises 37 and 38 have more than one possible answer since none of the fraction values are fixed. So, we determine that value of the fraction by our choice of numbers.

40. 3.75, or $3\frac{3}{4}$, cups

Possible Answers to Mathematical Reflections

1. To find the tax on a purchase, change the tax percent to a decimal. Multiply this decimal by the purchase price. Then the final bill will be the purchase price plus this tax. To save time, you can add 100% to the tax percent, then multiply this decimal by the purchase price to get the final bill in one step.

Example: How much will tax and total bill be for an item with a $35.00 purchase price at 6% tax? 6% becomes 0.06 as a decimal. $35 \times 0.06 = 2.10$. The tax will be $2.10 and the final bill will be $37.10. In one step, this would be $35 \times 1.06 = 37.10$.

2. This is just like figuring tax, except we need to subtract the discount from the purchase price, instead of adding it. So change the percent discount to a decimal. Multiply the decimal by the purchase price. This answer is the discount. Subtract the discount from the purchase price. The one-step shortcut is to subtract the percent discount from 100%, then change this new percent to a decimal and multiply by the purchase price.

3. a. Take the 5% amount and multiply by 3 to get 15%. Then double the 1% amount to get 2%. Add these two results.

    b. 10% is easy to get by doubling 5%. We can get any other whole percent by using multiples of 10%, 5%, and 1%.

4. Divide the amount of the tax by the percent tax to get 1% of the purchase price. Then multiply this answer by 100. In an example, if 6.5% tax came to $1.30, we would divide $1.30 by 6.5 to get 0.2. Then $0.20 is 1% of the cost of the item, so $20.00 is 100% of the cost.

5. We can think of 7 out of 35 as $\frac{7}{35}$, which is also $\frac{1}{5}$. As a decimal, it is 0.2, or 20%. In general, represent the numbers as a fraction, convert the fraction to a decimal, then to a percent.

Mathematical and Problem-Solving Goals

- Develop a strategy for finding the percent of discount an amount taken off a price represents

- Use percents in estimating taxes, tips, and discounts

- Solve problems involving percents

- Make and interpret circle graphs to represent data

Summary of Problems

Problem 5.1 Clipping Coupons

Students find what percent one number is of another in the context of buying an item when they have a coupon for a percent off, or a dollar amount off, the original cost.

Problem 5.2 How Much Can We Spend?

Problem 5.2 explores strategies for finding how much of the amount of money you can spend on food and still be able to pay the tax and tip on your dinner.

Problem 5.3 Making Circle Graphs

Students use data and percents, plus their knowledge of angles and angle measures, to make circle graphs to represent the data.

Overview

This investigation revisits the kinds of survey information presented in *Bits and Pieces I*, the first unit on fractions, decimals, and percents. Central to understanding surveys is the concept of percent, since answering interesting questions about survey data often requires finding a percent of a number as well as finding what percent a certain proportion of the survey represents. Remember that one of the useful properties of percents is that when we can express data as percents, we can compare different sets of data even when the sample sizes are different.

The investigation also asks students to work backwards to find what the cost of a meal was if the amount paid is known and the percent of tax included is known. The unit comes back to data in the last problem where students make circle graphs to represent and interpret data.

Mathematics Background

For background on percent operations and circle graphs, see pages 7–8.

	Suggested Pacing	Materials for Students	Materials for Teachers	ACE Assignments
All	4 days	Calculators		
5.1	1 day			1–6, 16–18, 23–30
5.2	$1\frac{1}{2}$ days		Transparency 4.1 (optional)	7–14, 19, 20, 32
5.3	1 day	Protractors or angle rulers, compasses; Labsheet 5.3	Transparency 5.3	15, 21, 22, 31
MR	$\frac{1}{2}$ day			

Goals

- Develop a strategy for finding the percent of discount an amount taken off a price represents

- Use percents in estimating taxes, tips, and discounts

In Problem 5.1, students deal with money, which involves decimal computation.

Launch 5.1

Raise interest in the problem by showing a page from a newspaper or magazine that has examples of coupons. The context should be familiar to students.

Suggested Question Ask:

- *What percent would I be saving if I used the coupon?*

Let students talk about this for a minute or so and then turn them loose to work on the problem. Indicate that you will be asking them to describe their methods and whether they found one method that would work for all the problems.

The introduction to the problem in the student edition gives an example that shows how thinking in pennies can be used as a way to handle decimals. You may want to skip this example and allow students to work on the coupon problem first, then share the strategy in the example.

Have students work in pairs.

Explore 5.1

As you observe the students working, encourage them to explore a variety of ways to solve the problem. If pairs are struggling, suggest they look back at the example given in the introduction to the problem.

Suggested Questions Ask:

- *How do you find the fraction of the cost the coupon represents?*

- *Would knowing this help solve the problem?*

Summarize 5.1

As a class, talk about all the ways student pairs found to solve the problem. Here are some strategies students have suggested for Question A:

> Scott and Tandra realized that they could figure out how much they get off for each dollar, which would give them the part per hundred, or the percent. They said that since 300 pennies, or 3 dollars, is the whole, they could think of it as three groups of 100 pennies, or 1 dollar. For a discount of 75 cents, 25 cents applies to each $1.00, or 25 pennies to each 100 pennies. Thus the discount is the same as a 25% reduction.

> Val and Lauren knew they could write 75 out of 300 as the fraction $\frac{75}{300}$. Then, they named an equivalent fraction, $\frac{25}{100}$, which is 25%.

> Using a calculator, Raj and Terry handled 75 out of 300 as a division problem, $75 \div 300$, getting the decimal 0.25, which they knew could be represented as 25%.

5.1 Clipping Coupons

Mathematical Goals

- Develop a strategy for finding the percent of discount an amount taken off a price represents
- Use percents in estimating taxes, tips, and discounts

Launch

Raise interest in the problem by showing a page from a newspaper or magazine that has examples of coupons. The context should be familiar to them.

Ask:

- *What percent would I be saving if I used the coupon?*

Let students talk about this for a minute or so and then turn them loose to work on the problem. Indicate that you will be asking them to describe their methods and whether they found one method that would work for all the problems.

The introduction to the problem in the student edition gives an example that shows how thinking in pennies can be used as a way to handle decimals. You may want to skip this example and allow students to work on the coupon problem first, then share the strategy in the example.

Have students work in pairs.

Explore

As you observe the students working, encourage them to explore a variety of ways to solve the problem. If pairs are struggling, suggest they look back at the example given in the introduction to the problem.

Ask:

- *How do you find the fraction of the cost the coupon represents?*
- *Would knowing this help solve the problem?*

Summarize

As a class, talk about all the ways student pairs found to solve the problem. Here are some strategies students have suggested for Question A:

Scott and Tandra realized that they could figure out how much they get off for each dollar, which would give them the part per hundred, or the percent. They said that since 300 pennies, or 3 dollars, is the whole, they could think of it as three groups of 100 pennies, or 1 dollar. For a discount of 75 cents, 25 cents applies to each $1.00, or 25 pennies to each 100 pennies. Thus the discount is the same as a 25% reduction.

Materials
- Student notebooks

continued on next page

Val and Lauren knew they could write 75 out of 300 as the fraction $\frac{75}{300}$. Then, they named an equivalent fraction, $\frac{25}{100}$, which is 25%.

Using a calculator, Raj and Terry handled 75 out of 300 as a division problem, $75 \div 300$, getting the decimal 0.25, which they knew could be represented as 25%.

ACE Assignment Guide for Problem 5.1

Core 1–6, 17
Other *Connections* 16, 18, *Extensions* 23–30

Adapted For suggestions about adapting ACE exercises, see the CMP *Special Needs Handbook*.

Answers to Problem 5.1

A. $0.75 \div 3.00 = 0.25$ or 25%

B. **1.** $0.50 \div 8.50 = 0.0588$ or about 6%

    2. $29.50 - 17.70 = 11.8$;
       $11.8 \div 29.50 = 0.4$ or 40%

C. $99. The question is what number times 0.25 gives $24.75. We can scale up by multiplying by 4 to get 1.00 and 99.00 (What number times 1 gives $99?). To check our thinking we can multiply $99 by 0.25. This gives $24.75. We can also think of the equation $0.25N = 24.75$. Fact families tell us that an equivalent statement is $N = 24.75 \div 0.25$. This gives $N = 99$.

D. $0.15N = 6.75$; $N = 6.75 \div 0.15$, or $45

How Much Can We Spend?

Goals

- Use percents in estimating or computing taxes, tips, and discounts

- Solve problems using percents

This problem is designed to engage the students in working backward, reversing the direction. Here, you know the final total for a bill and the percent of tax and tip, but you want to find the cost of the food before tax and tip. Through this problem, you can learn a great deal about how well your students are able to think about percents and to use percent bars as a model for representing the ideas, estimating solutions, and as a tool for thinking.

Launch 5.2

Set the scene with your students by describing the situation. Ask the students how this differs from the kinds of problems they have solved before in this investigation. Help them to articulate that now you know the final amount and need to find the original cost of the food.

This is a good problem for a Think-Pair-Share grouping. This gives students time to think on their own and then talk with a partner and finally share across two pairs of partners.

Explore 5.2

As the students are working, help those struggling by suggesting they represent the problem with a percent bar, and ask questions to be sure they are thinking of both the differences and the similarities between this problem and earlier ones.

Summarize 5.2

Ask a student to show his or her solution and explain the strategy used to solve the problem. Ask for additional solutions to be discussed with the class until you have all strategies displayed and talked about. Ask students to analyze the strategies used by different students and think about how efficient the strategy is and whether it is an approach or a way of thinking that can be used in different circumstances. In other words, is the strategy able to be generalized beyond this particular problem?

5.2 How Much Can We Spend?

PACING $1\frac{1}{2}$ days

Mathematical Goals

- Use percents in estimating or computing taxes, tips, and discounts
- Solve problems using percents

Launch

Set the scene with your students by describing the situation. Ask the students how this differs from the kinds of problems they have solved before in this investigation. Help them to articulate that now you know the final amount and need to find the original cost of the food.

This is a good problem for a Think-Pair-Share grouping. This gives students time to think on their own and then talk with a partner and finally share across two pairs of partners.

Explore

As the students are working, help those struggling by suggesting they represent the problem with a percent bar and ask questions to be sure they are thinking of both the differences and the similarities between this problem and earlier ones.

Summarize

Ask a student to show his or her solution and explain the strategy used to solve the problem. Ask for additional solutions to be discussed with the class until you have all strategies displayed and talked about. Ask students to analyze the strategies used by different students and think about how efficient the strategy is and whether it is an approach or a way of thinking that can be used in different circumstances. In other words, is the strategy able to be generalized beyond this particular problem?

Materials
- Student notebooks

ACE Assignment Guide for Problem 5.2

Differentiated Instruction
Solutions for All Learners

Core 7, 19
Other *Applications* 8–14; *Connections* 20; *Extensions* 32; unassigned choices from previous problems

Adapted For suggestions about adapting Exercise 13 and other ACE exercises, see the CMP *Special Needs Handbook*.

Answers to Problem 5.2

A. $50. You know that you need to add 20% (the tax and tip combined) of the food costs to the food costs to get the final bill of $60. So you can think in this way:

I need to partition the original costs into five equal parts to find the part representing the 20%. Then I need to add this part to the original to get the $60.

This means that the whole representing the $60 will be divided into six equal parts, as shown in the diagram (Figure 1), five for the food cost and one for the tax and tip. I take $\frac{5}{6}$ of the $60 to find the food costs. The mathematical sentence is: $\frac{5}{6}$ of $60 = $50. You could also find $\frac{1}{6}$ of $60 and multiply that number, $10, by 5 to get the cost for the food part of the bill.

Or if you think of the total cost as the whole, then you would equate the length of the bar with 120% and the amount you can pay for food as 100%. This means you are thinking:

120% → $60   20% → $10   100% → $50

Or you can reason that
$60 = Food + 0.2 × Food
$60 = 1.2 Food
$60 ÷ 1.2 = Food
$50 = Food

B. $64. You know that you need to add 25% of the food costs to the food costs to get the final bill of $80. So you can think in this way:

I need to partition the original costs into four equal parts to find the part representing the 25% that I need to add. This means that the whole representing the $80 will be divided into five equal parts, as shown (Figure 2). I take $\frac{4}{5}$ of the $80 to find the food costs. The mathematical sentence is: $\frac{4}{5}$ of $80 = $64. You could also find $\frac{1}{5}$ of $80 and multiply that number, $16, by 4 to get the cost for the food part of the bill, $64.

C. With the discount of 20%, the bill will be 80% of the original, or 0.8 × $68.79 = $55.032.

Again, the 10% off coupon means you will pay 90% of the discounted cost, or 0.9 × $55.032 = $49.5288 or about $49.53. Therefore, you will pay 0.8 × 0.9 = 0.72, or 72% of the original price. This means you get 28% off.

If you take 30% off the price, you will pay 70% of the price.

0.7 × $68.79 = $48.153, or $48.15

The two costs are not the same. Figure 3 may help students to see what is happening.

Figure 1

Figure 2

Figure 3

Goals

- Make and interpret circle graphs to represent data

- Solve problems involving percents

The mathematical connection in this problem is that, to find the sector needed to represent a given percent of a circle, students must find the given percent of 360°. Students must then measure with an angle ruler to construct a sector of a circle with that number of degrees. Calculators, angle rulers, and compasses should be available.

Launch 5.3

Have students look with you at the circle graphs in the introduction to the problem. Ask them to think about how the person who made the first graph figured out what 54% of the circle was, what 16% of the circle was, and so on. It's fine if students don't bring up angles and degrees at this time. The problem will present these ideas. Allow students to make sense of the suggestion and observe how information about percents and angle measures was used.

Have students work in pairs or groups of three. **Note:** Transparency 5.3 doesn't use keys on the circle graphs. You may want to point this out to students.

Explore 5.3

You may want to have them do their work on large sheets of paper that can be displayed during the summary for comparisons.

Summarize 5.3

Have groups discuss how they approached the problem. Some may have simply estimated the areas. Talk about the strengths and weaknesses of that strategy. Groups will probably suggest making the circle graph for dog owners by dividing a circle into four equal sections; one of those sections would represent 25%, and the other three would represent 75%. By now, many students know the relationship between 25% and $\frac{1}{4}$ and 75% and $\frac{3}{4}$.

Suggested Question If this strategy is suggested, ask:

- *How could you use that same strategy to create the circle graph for the crime-lab technicians data of 40% and 60%?*

This should lead to a discussion on how it is more difficult to divide a circle into ten equal sections than into four equal sections.

From here, you may ask whether anyone used angle measures to help them make the circle graphs. If yes, ask the students to explain. If not, ask how they could use angle measures to draw the different sections.

After the class has discussed the use of angle measures for constructing circle graphs, have students try the techniques on Question B. Discuss part (2) after the graphs are constructed.

5.3 Making Circle Graphs

Mathematical Goals

- Make and interpret circle graphs to represent data
- Solve problems involving percents

Launch

Have students look with you at the circle graphs in the introduction to the problem. Ask them to think about how the person who made the first graph figured out what 54% of the circle was, what 16% of the circle was, and so on. It's fine if students don't bring up angles and degrees at this time. The problem will present these ideas. Allow students to make sense of the suggestion and observe how information about percents and angle measures was used.

Have students work in pairs or groups of three.

Materials
- Transparency 5.3

Explore

You may want to have them do their work on large sheets of paper that can be displayed during the summary for comparisons.

Materials
- Labsheet 5.3
- Protractor or angle rulers
- Compasses

Summarize

Have groups discuss how they approached the problem. Some may have simply estimated the areas. Talk about the strengths and weaknesses of that strategy. Groups will probably suggest making the circle graph for dog owners by dividing a circle into four equal sections; one of those sections would represent 25%, and the other three would represent 75%. By now, many students know the relationship between 25% and $\frac{1}{4}$ and 75% and $\frac{3}{4}$.

If this strategy is suggested, ask:

- *How could you use that same strategy to create the circle graph for the crime-lab technicians data of 40% and 60%?*

This should lead to a discussion on how it is more difficult to divide a circle into ten equal sections than into four equal sections.

From here, you may ask whether anyone used angle measures to help them make the circle graphs. If yes, ask the students to explain. If not, ask how they could use angle measures to draw the different sections.

After the class has discussed the use of angle measures for constructing circle graphs, have students try the techniques on Question B. Discuss part (2) after the graphs are constructed.

Materials
- Student notebooks

ACE Assignment Guide
for Problem 5.3

Core 15

Other *Connections* 21, 22; *Extensions* 31; unassigned choices from previous problems

Adapted For suggestions about adapting ACE exercises, see the CMP *Special Needs Handbook*.

Answers to Problem 5.3

A.

Crime-Lab Technicians

Yes
40%
(144°)

No
60%
(216°)

Private Investigators

No
25%
(90°)

Yes
75%
(270°)

B. 1.

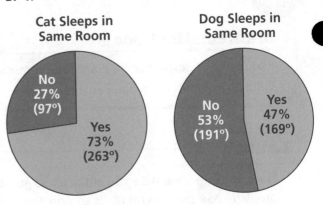

Cat Sleeps in Same Room

No
27%
(97°)

Yes
73%
(263°)

Dog Sleeps in Same Room

No
53%
(191°)

Yes
47%
(169°)

Point out to students that you usually round to the nearest whole number of degrees when making a circle graph.

2. More cat owners let their pets sleep in the same room; about $\frac{3}{4}$ of the people surveyed. Less than half of the dog owners let their pets sleep in the same room.

The student edition pages for this
investigation begin on the next page.

Notes _____

_____

_____

_____

More About Percents

In *Bits and Pieces I*, you changed numbers in fraction or decimal form to percent form. In the last investigation, you built on this to find an amount given as a percent of a total. For example, you started with the price of an item and the percent discount offered on the item, and you computed how much money you would save.

Now you will face similar situations, but you will be given different pieces of information.

5.1 Clipping Coupons

Newspapers often have coupons for discounts on many different things. One coupon for shampoo is shown.

The regular price for the shampoo is $5.00. Alicia wants to figure out what percent discount this is. She thinks about the problem this way:

"I need to find what percent $1.50 is of $5.00. I can think of these amounts in pennies. The fraction I want to represent as a percent is $\frac{150}{500}$, which is equivalent to $\frac{30}{100}$. This means that the discount is 30%!"

62   Bits and Pieces III

Notes _____

_____

_____

_____

Problem **5.1** Finding Percent Discounts

A. What percent discount do you get with this coupon? Try to find more than one way to solve this problem. Be prepared to explain your methods.

B. Estimate each percent discount for the sales below. Explain.

1.

2.

C. The 25% discount on a skateboard is $24.75. What is the cost without the discount?

D. The 15% discount on a sweater is $6.75. What is the original cost?

ACE **Homework starts on page 67.**

STUDENT PAGE

Notes _____

_____

_____

_____

STUDENT PAGE

(63) 112

5.2 How Much Can We Spend?

Sometimes you have to figure out whether you have enough money in your pocket to buy an item that you want. Suppose you go out to dinner with friends and put all of your money together. What can you buy?

Problem 5.2 Solving Percent Problems

A. Your group has $60 altogether for pizza. The tax is 5% and you want to leave a 15% tip on the price of the food before sales tax. What is the maximum amount your group can spend and not go over $60? Explain your reasoning. Show any diagrams you make to help figure out the answer.

B. You and your friends go out to eat again. This time you have $80 altogether. The tax is 7% and you want to leave an 18% tip. What is the maximum amount your group can spend and not go over $80? Explain. Show any diagrams you make to help figure out the answer.

C. To celebrate your election to the student council, your grandparents take you shopping. You have a 20%-off coupon. The cashier takes 20% off the $68.79 bill. Your grandmother remembers that she has an additional coupon for 10% off. The cashier takes the 10% off what the cash register shows. Does this result in the same amount as 30% off the original bill? Explain.

ACE Homework starts on page 67.

Notes _____

_____

_____

_____

Making Circle Graphs

Circle graphs, or pie charts, are special kinds of graphs used to show how a whole (100%) is divided into several categories. They are often used to survey data. For example, dog and cat owners who said their pets had bad breath were asked, "Which of these methods do you use most frequently to take care of your pet's bad breath?" Here are the results:

**Owner Solutions for
Bad Breath in Pets**

	Dog Owners	Cat Owners
Toothpaste	54%	53%
Mouthwash	16%	14%
Dental floss	7%	24%
Other	23%	9%
Total	100%	100%

Notice that the total of each column in the table is 100%.

Now, here are the results displayed in two pie charts.

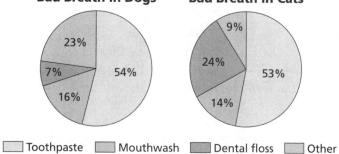

Owner Solutions for Bad Breath in Dogs

Owner Solutions for Bad Breath in Cats

☐ Toothpaste ▨ Mouthwash ▨ Dental floss ☐ Other

Notes _____

_____

_____

_____

Problem 5.3 Making Circle Graphs

Study the circle graphs below. Use what you know about angle measures, circles, and percents to figure out how they were made. Then work on the questions below.

Owner Solutions for Bad Breath in Dogs

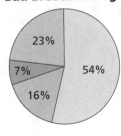

Owner Solutions for Bad Breath in Cats

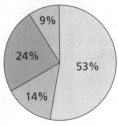

☐ Toothpaste ☐ Mouthwash ☐ Dental floss ☐ Other

A. Private investigators and crime-lab technicians were asked, "Would you say your job is exciting?" Use the results in the table to make two circle graphs.

	Crime-Lab Technicians	Private Investigators
Yes	40%	75%
No	60%	25%
Total	100%	100%

B. 1. Cat and dog owners were asked, "Does your pet sleep in the same room with you?" Use the results in the table to make two circle graphs.

	Cat Owners	Dog Owners
Yes	73%	47%
No	27%	53%
Total	100%	100%

2. How do the answers of the cat owners and dog owners compare?

ACE Homework starts on page 67.

Notes _____

_____

_____

_____

Applications

Solve Exercises 1–4, and then show how you found your answer.

1. What is 5% of 40?

2. What is 22% of 220?

3. 5 is what percent of 40?

4. 75 is what percent of 80?

Go Online
PHSchool.com

For: Multiple-Choice Skills
Practice
Web Code: ama-6554

5. **Multiple Choice** What is 75% of 80?

   A. 20   **B.** 40   **C.** 60   **D.** 75

6. **Multiple Choice** 22 is what percent of 220?

   F. 10%   **G.** 22%   **H.** 44%   **J.** 198%

7. A music store reported 15 sales for every 100 people who visited the store last year. What percent of the visitors bought something?

8. As part of a probability activity, Roberto is counting the occurrence of different letters in a paragraph in his biology book. In the first 1,000 letters, he finds 50 b's. What percent of the letters are b's?

9. Estimate what percent discount Ling will receive if she buys the microscope kit advertised below. Explain.

MICROSCOPE KITS

Customers usually pay..... **$7.95**
Students save by
paying only.................. **$6.76**

Investigation 5 More About Percents   **67**

10. The auto shop class conducted a survey to determine which math teacher's car was the most popular with the students. These were the results:

a. What percent of the votes did Mr. Alberto's car receive? Explain.

b. What percent of the votes did Ms. Dole's car receive?

c. One student said Ms. Grant's car received 48% of the votes. Is he correct? Explain.

Math Teacher	Student Votes
Ms. Grant	48
Ms. Dole	35
Mr. Alberto	12
Ms. Bock	75

11. Juan, Makayla, and Sam belong to an after-school group. They joined the group at different times after the beginning of school. The chart shows their attendance so far at the various events, including meetings, held by the group.

Attendance Since Joining Group

Member	Events Attended	Total Events Held
Juan	20	30
Makayla	11	18
Sam	7	12

a. Suppose the attendance pattern of all three students remains about the same for the next 30 events. Who will have the highest percent of attendance at the 30 events? Explain.

b. There are 120 events planned for the rest of the year. How many would you expect each of the students to attend if they keep the same percent of attendance? Explain.

12. Three children put their money together to buy their parents a present. Together they have $91. If the state sales tax is 4%, what is the maximum amount of money they can spend on the gift?

13. You and your friends are going out to eat. You decide to pool your money and order several dishes and appetizers to share. You have $75 altogether. If the tax is 5% and you want to leave a 15% tip (on the price before tax), what is the maximum you can spend?

Notes _____

_____

_____

_____

14. Violeta is shopping. She has a coupon for 20% off her total purchase. The tax is 5%.

   a. Violeta has $60 to spend. How much of this can she use (after the discount is figured) and still have enough to pay the tax?

   b. Violeta realizes that she has extra money to pay the tax and can spend the entire $60 on merchandise. Use the original cost of the merchandise before the 20% is taken off. How much can the total amount to? Explain.

15. a. Dog and cat owners were asked, "How often do you feed your pet?" Make two circle graphs of the results shown in the table.

Feeding Times for Pets

Time of Day	Cat Owners	Dog Owners
Night only	4%	2%
Morning only	6%	10%
Morning and night	42%	46%
Anytime	48%	42%
Total	100%	100%

   b. Compare the feeding patterns of dog owners to cat owners.

   c. Suppose the radius of each circle graph is 6 cm. Find the area of the "Morning only" section of each circle graph.

Connections

16. In a survey of 100 dog owners about their pets' habits, 39% said that their dogs eat bugs. How many dog owners surveyed said this?

17. In a survey of 80 students, 40% said they had a savings account of their own. How many students surveyed said this?

18. Suppose 300 tarantula owners were surveyed, and 26% said they let their spiders crawl on them. How many tarantula owners surveyed said this?

Investigation 5 More About Percents　　**69**

Notes _____

_____

_____

_____

19. In a survey of 80 student artists, 6% said they had sold at least one of their works of art. How many students surveyed said this?

20. It is Crazy Coupon Day at the school store. At each counter students are given a coupon to use on any item at that counter. For each of the following items, compute the percent of discount.

   a. $5.00 off a $25 item

   b. $2.50 off a $20 item

   c. $8.00 off a $160 item

   d. If you know the discount and the price, how do you find the percent discount that the coupon gives?

21. A sugarless gum company used to state:

Homework Help **Online**
PHSchool.com
For: Help with Exercise 21
Web Code: ame-6521

   "Nine out of ten dentists surveyed recommended sugarless gum for their patients who chew gum."

   Sketch a circle graph showing the percent of dentists who recommended sugarless gum for their patients who chewed gum and the percent of dentists who did not.

22. The chart below shows the percent of various reasons for moving.

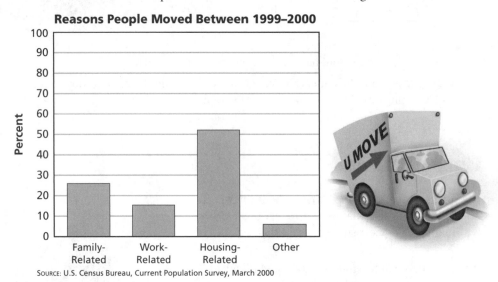

Reasons People Moved Between 1999–2000

SOURCE: U.S. Census Bureau, Current Population Survey, March 2000

   a. Sketch a circle graph of the data in the chart and label each section.

   b. Which representation of the data would you use to argue that most people surveyed moved for housing-related reasons? Explain.

70   Bits and Pieces III

Notes _____

_____

_____

_____

Extensions

For Exercises 23–28, find numbers that make each sentence true.

23. $\frac{6}{\blacksquare} = \frac{18}{\blacksquare} = \frac{\blacksquare}{20}$ **24.** $\frac{12}{\blacksquare} = \frac{\blacksquare}{36} = \frac{\blacksquare}{12}$ **25.** $\frac{\blacksquare}{8} = \frac{16}{\blacksquare} = \frac{\blacksquare}{4}$

26. $\frac{2}{3} < \frac{\blacksquare}{9}$ **27.** $\frac{2}{3} = \frac{\blacksquare}{9}$ **28.** $\frac{2}{3} > \frac{\blacksquare}{9}$

29. 80 is 40% of what number? Explain.

30. 220 is 20% of what number? Explain.

31. When people are allowed to choose more than one answer to a survey question, the percents for the categories may add to more than 100%. For example, in one survey people were asked why they owned a pet. They were allowed to mark off more than one reason, so the percents add to more than 100%. Here are the results.

Reasons People Give for Owning Pets

Reason	Dog Owners	Cat Owners
Love/Companionship	88%	93%
Security	39%	0%
Protection	35%	0%
Entertainment	26%	33%
Catching Rodents	0%	16%
Breeding (to make money)	16%	6%
Children Grown/Spouse Died	4%	10%
Total	208%	158%

When percents add to more than 100%, you can make a bar graph to show the information.

a. Make bar graphs to display the data shown in the table. Before you make your bar graphs, think about these questions:

- What kinds of data will you display in your graphs?
- What will you show on the horizontal axis (the *x*-axis)?
- What will you show on the vertical axis (the *y*-axis)?
- What scale will you use for the *y*-axis?

b. Write a paragraph comparing the responses of dog owners to cat owners in this survey.

Notes _____

_____

_____

_____

32. Copy machines use percents to enlarge and reduce the size of copies.

   a. The picture below has been enlarged to 200% with a copy machine. Suppose you want to return this enlarged copy to its original size. What percent should you enter on the copy machine?

   b. Suppose you have a copy that is reduced to 50% of its original size. In order to return it to its original size, what percent should you enter into the copy machine?

   c. A copy is $1\frac{1}{2}$ times the size of the original. What percent should you enter in a copy machine to return it to its original size?

   d. A copy is $\frac{3}{4}$ of its original size. What percent should you enter in a copy machine to return it to its original size?

72   Bits and Pieces III

Notes _____

_____

_____

_____

Mathematical Reflections 5

In this investigation you studied situations for which you need to find the percent one number is of another number so that you could describe the situation or compare it to another situation. The following questions will help you summarize what you have learned.

Think about your answers to these questions. Discuss your ideas with other students and your teacher. Then write a summary of your findings in your notebook.

1. Describe at least two ways to find what percent one number is of another. Use an example to help explain why each method works.

2. Describe how to find what the original cost is if you know the amount and the percent of the discount. Use an example to explain your method.

3. Suppose you have a fixed amount of money to spend and you have to pay a percent of it for tax. How do you find the amount you can spend so that you will have enough for the purchase and for the tax? Use an example to explain your strategy.

4. Describe how to make a circle graph. Use an example to explain your strategy.

Notes _____

_____

_____

_____

Investigation 5

ACE
Assignment Choices

Differentiated Instruction
Solutions for All Learners

Problem 5.1
Core 1–6, 17
Other *Connections* 16, 18, *Extensions* 23–30

Problem 5.2
Core 7, 19
Other *Applications* 8–14, *Connections* 20;
Extensions 32; unassigned choices from previous problems

Problem 5.3
Core 15
Other *Connections* 21, 22, *Extensions* 31;
unassigned choices from previous problems

Adapted For suggestions about adapting Exercise 13 and other ACE exercises, see the CMP *Special Needs Handbook*.

Applications

1. 2; Possible explanation: 10% of 40 is 4, so 5% must be 2.

2. 48.4; 1% of 220 is 2.2, so 22% is
$22 \times 1\% = 22 \times 2.2 = 48.4$.

3. 12.5%; 5 out of 40 is $\frac{5}{40} = \frac{1}{8} = 0.125$, or 12.5%.

4. 93.75%; 75 out of 80 is $\frac{75}{80} = \frac{15}{16} = 0.9375$, or 93.75%.

5. C

6. F

7. 15%

8. 5%

9. About 15%; the discount is $1.19 out of $7.95, or $\frac{119}{795}$, which gives 0.14969 on a calculator, or about 15%.

10. **a.** About 7%; of the 170 votes cast, 12 were for Mr. Alberto's car, and $\frac{12}{170}$ gives 0.070588 on a calculator, or about 7%.

    b. About 21%; Ms. Dole's car received 35 out of 170 votes, or $\frac{35}{170}$, which gives 0.20588 on a calculator, or about 21%.

    c. No; Ms. Grant's car received 48 votes, but this can't be 48% of the votes because the number of students who voted was not 100.

11. **a.** Juan; Juan's percent of attendance is about 67%, Makayla's is about 61%, and Sam's is about 58%.

    b. Juan: $0.67 \times 120 \approx 80$; Makayla: $0.61 \times 120 \approx 73$; Sam: $0.58 \times 120 \approx 70$

12. $87.50

13. $62.50

14. **a.** $57.14; $71.42 is the original price, so $57.14 is the price she would pay out of her $60 after the 20% discount to still allow enough money to pay tax.

    b. If tax is not an issue, then she only needs to pay 80% of the marked price of her items. We want to know what number 60 is 80% of. This is $75.00.

15. a. **When Cat Owners Feed Their Pets**

Night Only 4% (14°)
Morning Only 6% (22°)
Anytime 48% (173°)
Morning and night 42% (151°)

When Dog Owners Feed Their Pets

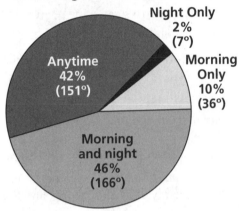

Night Only 2% (7°)
Morning Only 10% (36°)
Anytime 42% (151°)
Morning and night 46% (166°)

b. Possible answers: More dog owners than cat owners have set feeding times for their pets. Dog and cat feeding times are very similar.

c. Cat owners: about 6.8 cm² (3.14 × 36 × 0.06 = 6.8); dog owners: about 11.3 cm² (3.14 × 36 × 0.1 = 11.3)

Connections

16. 39 dog owners

17. 32 students

18. 78 tarantula owners

19. about 5 students

20. a. 20%   **b.** 12.5%   **c.** 5%

d. Since you multiply the item price by the percent to find the amount off, you do the reverse to find the percent. You divide the price into the discount to find the percent

off. In words and fact families the problem looks like this:

Percent off × cost = discount, or
Percent off = discount ÷ cost.

21. Dentists who recommend sugarless gum for their patients who chew gum

Dentists who do not recommend sugarless gum

22. a.

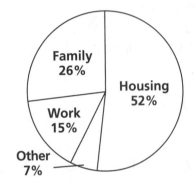

Family 26%
Housing 52%
Work 15%
Other 7%

b. Answers will vary. Some may find it easier to show with the circle graph, as the sector for housing is more than half the circle graph and, thus, is more than all of the other sectors combined.

Extensions

23. Possible answer: $\frac{6}{40} = \frac{18}{120} = \frac{3}{20}$

24. Possible answer: $\frac{12}{24} = \frac{18}{36} = \frac{6}{12}$

25. Possible answer: $\frac{2}{8} = \frac{16}{64} = \frac{1}{4}$

26. Possible answer: $\frac{2}{3} < \frac{\blacksquare}{9}$ (The black box can be replaced with any number greater than 6.)

27. $\frac{2}{3} = \frac{6}{9}$

28. Possible answer: $\frac{2}{3} > \frac{\blacksquare}{9}$ (The black box can be replaced with any number less than 6.)

29. 200; if 40% is 80, then 10% must be 20, and 100% must be 20 × 10 = 200.

30. 1,100; if 20% is 220, then 10% must be 110, and 100% must be 110 × 10 = 1,100.

31. a. (Figure 4)

   b. Possible answer: The majority of people responded that they have pets for love and companionship. The responses seem to indicate that cats are not as popular for security and protection as dogs are, but that dogs are not as good at catching rodents as are cats. Entertainment as a response was stated for both dogs and cats.

32. a. 50%   **b.** 200%

   c. 67%   **d.** 133%

Possible Answers to Mathematical Reflections

1. Using the fraction method of finding what percent 30 is of 120, you could reason as follows: 30 out of 120 can be expressed as $\frac{30}{120} = \frac{1}{4} = \frac{25}{100}$, which is 25%. Alternatively, we can change the fraction $\frac{30}{120}$ to a decimal by dividing the numerator by the denominator, giving $30 \div 120 = 0.25$, which is the same as 25%.

2. If the amount is $25 and the discount was 15%, the equation to solve is $C - 0.15C = \$25$.

This is the same equation as $0.85C = \$25$. Compute $25 \div 0.85$ to get an original cost of $29.41.

3. Suppose that you have $100 and that the sales tax is 7%. So the $100 has to represent 107% of the cost of the item. You can divide $100 by 1.07 to find the amount you can spend, about $93.45. To check, you can take 7% of 93.45 and add it to 93.45 and see if you are near $100.

4. Because there are 360° in a circle, for whatever percent you need to find, say, 23% of 360°, rewrite 23% as the fraction $\frac{23}{100}$ and then find an equivalent fraction with a denominator of 360. Multiply by $\frac{3.6}{3.6}$ to make the denominator 360, and the numerator becomes 82.8°. Mark off a section of the circle with a central angle measure of 82.8°.

Looking Back and Looking Ahead

1. a. McNair's Passer Rating: 100.4

   Step-by-step solution:
   step 1 = 1.625;   step 2 = 1.259;
   step 3 = 1.200;   step 4 = 1.938;
   step 5 = 100.4

   Manning's Passer Rating: 99.0

Figure 4

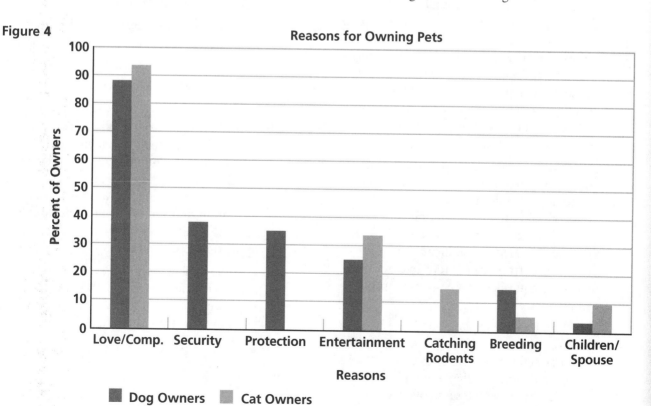

Reasons for Owning Pets

Step-by-step solution:
step 1 = 1.848;   step 2 = 1.135;
step 3 = 1.025;   step 4 = 1.933;
step 5 = 99.0

Culpepper's Passer Rating: 96.4
Step-by-step solution:
step 1 = 1.749;   step 2 = 1.166;
step 3 = 1.101;   step 4 = 1.769;
step 5 = 96.4

b. Steve McNair

2. a. Highest is $25.16 and lowest is $19.87.

b. The total cost is $67.54.

c. 48%. This is for the sum of both the strongly and somewhat influenced categories.

3. Possible descriptions for addition: Write the decimals as fractions and use fraction algorithms; add by the value of the place the number is in (keep track by lining up the decimal points so that numbers with the same place value are in the same column).

Possible description for subtraction: Use the same algorithms as addition, except subtract.

Possible descriptions for multiplication: Change the decimals to fractions with powers of 10 in the denominator, multiply the numerators and the denominators, rename the fraction product as a decimal;
look at patterns in the factors and product, multiply as we do whole numbers,
adjust the answer by counting and adding the number of decimal places in the two decimal factors. Then, place the decimal point in the whole-number product so it has the same number of decimal places as the total of the number of places in the factors.

Possible descriptions for division: Change the decimals to fractions with powers of 10 in the denominator. Adjust as needed so both fractions have the same denominator or place value. Next, divide the numerators (whole numbers) to find the quotient; think of the decimals as fractions in order to determine what the equivalent whole-number problem would be.

4. a. 40.82; Possible explanation:
Write one number above the other being sure to line up the decimal points so that you add digits that have the same place value.

$$\begin{array}{r} 23.4 \\ + \underline{17.42} \\ 40.82 \end{array}$$

b. 25.47; Possible explanation:
Write one number above the other being sure to line up the decimal points so that you subtract digits that have the same place value.

$$\begin{array}{r} 43.09 \\ - \underline{17.62} \\ 25.47 \end{array}$$

c. 4.212; Possible explanation: Multiply as if there were no decimal points. Then make sure the product has as many decimal places as in the two factors combined.

$$3.51 \times 1.2 \rightarrow 351 \times 12 = 4212$$

Since there are two decimal places in 3.51 and one place in 1.2, there should be a total of three places in the product. The whole-number product 4212 should be rewritten as 4.212.

d. 3.9; Possible explanation: Rewrite the decimals as whole numbers, either by thinking about them as fractions or multiplying both by 10. Then divide the whole numbers. This quotient will be the same as the quotient of the original decimal numbers.

$$11.7 \div 3 = \frac{117}{10} \div \frac{3}{1} = \frac{117}{10} \div \frac{30}{10} =$$
$$117 \div 30 = \frac{117}{30} = 3\frac{27}{30} = 3\frac{9}{10} = 3.9$$

5. a. Possible explanation: The percent equivalent of 0.73 is 73%.

You can write the decimal as a fraction with 100 in the denominator. This gives $\frac{73}{100}$. Since percent means out of 100, the percent is 73%. Another example is $1.23 = \frac{123}{100}$ or 123%.

b. Possible explanation: To find what percent 23 is of 138, we need to remember the relationship this implies. We are to find a solution for x in the mathematical sentence: $x\%$ of $138 = 23$. Since $x\%$ *times* 138 gave 23, we can find what percent by *dividing* 23 by 138. This gives 0.166666. . . or approximately 17 percent.

c. Possible explanation: To find 34% of 249, we are solving the sentence 34% of $249 = x$. Here we can write the percent as a decimal and multiply it by 249 to find the answer, 84.66.

Assigning the Unit Project

In part I, students are asked to select three items from a catalog and fill out an order blank as if they were going to purchase the items. They must find shipping cost (which is a percent of the total cost) and the sales tax (based on the rate for their state). They are also asked to compute what the items would cost if given discounts were applied. In part II, students are asked to work backwards to find the maximum cost of the three items so that Uri would be able to pay the tax and shipping as well. They are also asked to find three items that would come closest to the $125 Uri got for his birthday.

The blackline masters for the project and the order blank are provided. Depending on the time you have for students to work on the project, you may choose to only assign part I. Below is a scoring rubric. This is followed by samples of student work for Part I and a teacher's comments on each sample.

Grading the Unit Project

A possible scoring rubric and two sample projects with teacher comments follow.

Suggested Scoring Rubric

This rubric for scoring the project employs a scale that runs from 0 to 4, with a 4+ for work that goes beyond what has been asked for in some unique way. You may use this rubric as presented here or modify it to fit your district's requirements for evaluating and reporting students' work and understanding.

4+ EXEMPLARY RESPONSE

- Complete, with clear, coherent explanations
- Shows understanding of the mathematical concepts and procedures
- Satisfies all essential conditions of the problem and goes beyond what is asked for in some unique way

4 COMPLETE RESPONSE

- Complete, with clear, coherent explanations
- Shows understanding of the mathematical concepts and procedures
- Satisfies all essential conditions of the problem

3 REASONABLY COMPLETE RESPONSE

- Reasonably complete; may lack detail in explanations
- Shows understanding of most of the mathematical concepts and procedures
- Satisfies most of the essential conditions of the problem

2 PARTIAL RESPONSE

- Gives response; explanation may be unclear or lack detail
- Shows some understanding of some of the mathematical concepts and procedures
- Satisfies some essential conditions of the problem

1 INADEQUATE RESPONSE

- Incomplete; explanation is insufficient or not understandable
- Shows little understanding of the mathematical concepts and procedures
- Fails to address essential conditions of problem

0 NO ATTEMPT

- Irrelevant response
- Does not attempt a solution
- Does not address conditions of the problem

Sample #1

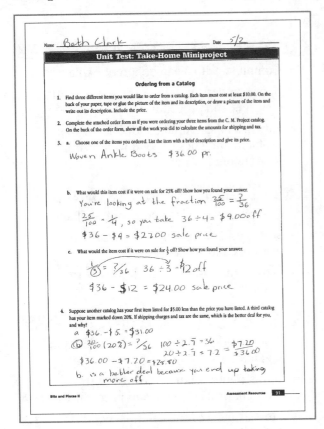

Ordering from a Catalog

1. Find three different items you would like to order from a catalog. Each item must cost at least $10.00. On the back of your paper, tape or glue the picture of the item and its description, or draw a picture of the item and write out its description. Include the price.

2. Complete the attached order form as if you were ordering your three items from the C. M. Project catalog. On the back of the order form, show all the work you did to calculate the amounts for shipping and tax.

3. a. Choose one of the items you ordered. List the item with a brief description and give its price.

    Woven Ankle Boots $36.00 pr.

    b. What would this item cost if it were on sale for 25% off? Show how you found your answer.

     You're looking at the fraction $\frac{25}{100} = \frac{?}{36}$

     $\frac{25}{100} = \frac{1}{4}$, so you take $36 \div 4 = \$9.00$ off

     $\$36 - \$4 = \$27.00$ sale price

    c. What would the item cost if it were on sale for $\frac{1}{3}$ off? Show how you found your answer.

     $\frac{1}{3} = \frac{?}{36}$. $36 \div 3 = \$12$ off

     $\$36 - \$12 = \$24.00$ sale price

4. Suppose another catalog has your first item listed for $5.00 less than the price you have listed. A third catalog has your item marked down 20%. If shipping charges and tax are the same, which is the better deal for you, and why?

     a. $\$36 - \$5 = \$31.00$

     b. $\frac{20}{100}(20\%) = \frac{?}{36}$ $100 \div 2.\overline{7} = 36$ $\$7.20$
     $20 \div 2.\overline{7} = 7.2$ $\$36.00$
     $\$36.00 - \$7.20 = \$28.80$

     b. is a better deal because you end up taking more off.

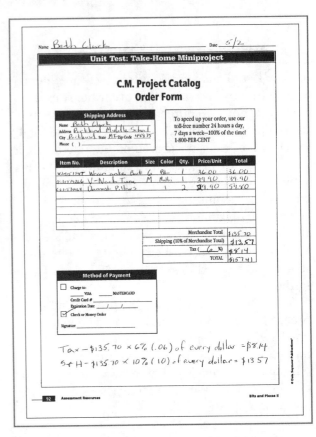

C.M. Project Catalog
Order Form

Shipping Address
Name _Beth Clark_
Address _Richland Middle School_
City _Richland_ State _MI_ Zip Code _449 75_
Phone ( )

To speed up your order, use our toll-free number 24 hours a day, 7 days a week—100% of the time! 1-800-PER-CENT

Item No.	Description	Size	Color	Qty.	Price/Unit	Total
W145·1145T	Woven ankle Boot G	6	Bl.	1	36.00	36.00
9·157·1326G	V-Neck Tunic	M	Mult.	1	39.90	39.90
6·157·5464	Damask Pillows			2	29.90	59.80

Merchandise Total	$135.70
Shipping (10% of Merchandise Total)	$13.57
Tax (6 %)	$8.14
TOTAL	$157.41

Method of Payment
☐ Charge to:
___ VISA ___ MASTERCARD
Credit Card # ___
Expiration Date __/__/__
☑ Check or Money Order
Signature ___

Tax — $135.70 × 6% (.06) of every dollar = $8.14
S&H — $135.70 × 10% (.10) of every dollar = $13.57

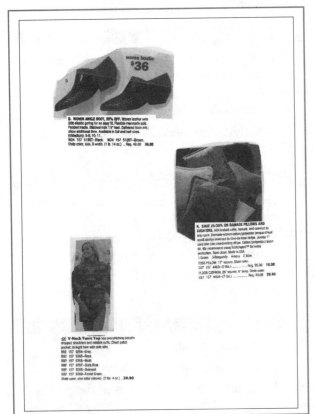

A Teacher's Comments on Sample 1

Beth received a 4 for her work. She meets the demands of the task by successfully addressing all the essential conditions of the questions. Her explanations of her reasoning are very clear. For example, when she computes the tax and shipping for her order, she shows how she multiplied the merchandise total by the decimal equivalents of the needed percents. She also clearly shows her thinking in computing the 25%, $\frac{1}{3}$, and 20% discounts. Beth shows a considerable amount of understanding of rational numbers and flexibility in working with them. She uses multiple methods when performing operations involving rational numbers.

Sample #2

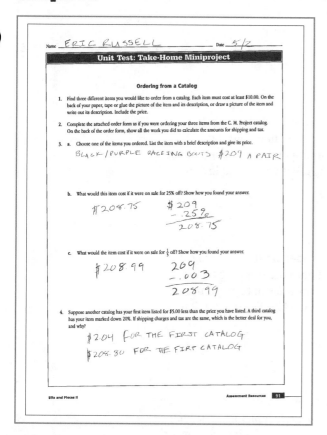

Name ERIC RUSSELL   Date 5/2

Unit Test: Take-Home Miniproject

Ordering from a Catalog

1. Find three different items you would like to order from a catalog. Each item must cost at least $10.00. On the back of your paper, tape or glue the picture of the item and its description, or draw a picture of the item and write out its description. Include the price.

2. Complete the attached order form as if you were ordering your three items from the C. M. Project catalog. On the back of the order form, show all the work you did to calculate the amounts for shipping and tax.

3. a. Choose one of the items you ordered. List the item with a brief description and give its price.

   BLACK/PURPLE RACING BOOTS $209 A PAIR

   b. What would this item cost if it were on sale for 25% off? Show how you found your answer.

   $208.75 $209
              -.25%
              208.75

   c. What would the item cost if it were on sale for ⅓ off? Show how you found your answer.

   $208.99   209
              -.003
              208.99

4. Suppose another catalog has your first item listed for $5.00 less than the price you have listed. A third catalog has your item marked down 20%. If shipping charges and tax are the same, which is the better deal for you, and why?

   $204 FOR THE FIRST CATALOG
   $208.80 FOR THE FIRT CATALOG

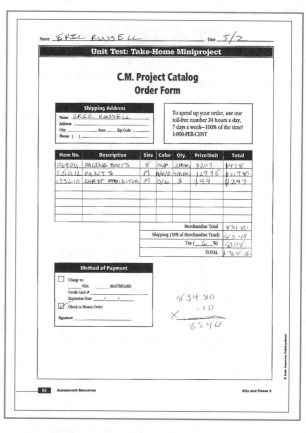

Name ERIC RUSSELL   Date 5/2

Unit Test: Take-Home Miniproject

C.M. Project Catalog
Order Form

Shipping Address

Name ERIC RUSSELL
Address
City _____ State ____ Zip Code _____
Phone ( )

To speed up your order, use our toll-free number 24 hours a day, 7 days a week—100% of the time! 1-800-PER-CENT

Item No.	Description	Size	Color	Qty.	Price/Unit	Total
069011	RACING BOOTS	8	blk/p	2 (pair)	$209	$418
251272	PANTS	M	b/g/o	4 (pairs)	$29.95	$119.80
173210	CHEST PROTECTOR	M	b/g	3	$99	$297
					Merchandise Total	834.80
					Shipping (10% of Merchandise Total)	83.48
					Tax (6 %)	50.08
					TOTAL	968.36

Method of Payment

☐ Charge to:
  ____ VISA ____ MASTERCARD
  Credit Card #
  Expiration Date __/__/__
☑ Check or Money Order
Signature

834.80
X   .10
83.40

A Teacher's Comments on Sample 2

Eric received a 1 for his work. His response is weak. He does find tax and shipping for his order but does not show or explain how he found the 6% sales tax. In the last question, he does not show or explain how he came up with the sales price after a 20% discount. I feel that a student's explanation is as important as the correct answer. The lack of explanation is critical to the quality of Eric's paper. I am also concerned about his misconceptions about discounts. In questions 3 and 4, he subtracts to find the sales price for the discounted item, showing no understanding of rational numbers. It is not clear why he subtracted for these problems when he multiplied to find the 10% shipping charge. Eric's work suggests that he needs additional instruction on working with rational numbers.

Unit Project

Ordering From a Catalog

Buying things from catalogs is something that families do frequently. But you might not ever have been the family member that filled out the order form. This project gives you a chance to show what you have learned about decimals and percents as you dream about things that you would love to order from a favorite catalog.

Part 1:

Choose a catalog and fill out the order form provided on the next page. Be sure that you correctly compute the taxes and figure the shipping costs for your items. Information on what the shipping costs are will be in your catalog. You also need to know the sales tax on merchandise in your state.

Steps in Filling Out the Order

Step 1:

1. Find three different items you would like to order from a catalog. Each item must cost at least $10. In your report, include a picture or sketch of the items. Tape or glue the picture of the item and its description, or draw a picture of the item and write out its description. Include the price with your picture or drawing.

Step 2:

2. Complete the attached order form as if you were ordering your three items from the C. M. Project catalog.

Record all the work you do to calculate the amounts for shipping and tax.

Notes _____

_____

_____

_____

3. **a.** Choose one of the items you ordered. List the item with a brief description and give its price. Then answer these questions:

   b. What would this item cost if it were on sale for 25% off? Show how you found your answer.

   c. What would the item cost if it were on sale for $\frac{1}{3}$ off? Show how you found your answer.

4. Suppose another catalog has your first item listed for $5 less than the price you have listed. A third catalog has your item marked down 20%. If shipping charges and sales tax are the same, which is the better deal for you, and why?

Part 2:

5. Uri got $125 for his twelfth birthday and is going to use your catalog to order three items. Uri's state has a tax rate of 6%. Assume that the shipping costs are 9% of the cost before tax.

   a. Find the most that the three items can cost, before tax and shipping, so that Uri has enough money to order the items. Show your work and explain your reasoning.

   b. Find three items in the catalog that use up as much of Uri's birthday money as possible. Remember the sales tax and shipping charges.

Notes _____

_____

_____

_____

Looking Back and Looking Ahead

Unit Review

Working on the problems in this unit helped you to develop strategies for estimating and for computing with decimals and percents. You learned how to

Go Online
PHSchool.com
For: Vocabulary Review
Puzzle
Web Code: amj-6051

- relate operations on decimals to the same operations on common fractions
- use place value ideas to look for patterns in answers to computation problems
- use your knowledge of whole numbers, fractions, decimals, and percents to find shortcuts for some computations (algorithms)

Use Your Understanding: Decimals and Percents

The National Football League (NFL™) has developed an algorithm for rating the passing performance of any player who attempts a pass during a season. Since the quarterback position requires passing, the system is most often used to rate quarterback performance.

Four categories are used in a passer rating:

    percent of passes completed

    average yards gained per pass

    percent of passes for touchdowns

    percent of passes intercepted

Use the algorithm and data on the next page to find the passing performance of the three highest-rated quarterbacks of the 2003 NFL regular season.

76   Bits and Pieces III

STUDENT PAGE

Notes _____

_____

_____

_____

STUDENT PAGE

Passer Rating Formula

- Calculate the percent of completed passes, or pass completions out of pass attempts. Subtract 30 from the percent, then multiply by 0.05.
- Calculate the average yards gained per pass, or pass yardage out of pass attempts. Subtract 3 from the average and multiply by 0.25.
- Calculate the percent of touchdown passes, or touchdown passes out of pass attempts. Multiply the percent by 0.2.
- Calculate the percent of interceptions, or interceptions out of pass attempts. Multiply the percent by 0.25. Subtract the product from 2.375.
- Determine the overall passer rating. Find the sum of the values from steps 1–4. Divide the sum by 6 and multiply by 100.

1. a. Calculate the passer rating for each quarterback.

2003 NFL Quarterback Statistics

Player	Pass Attempts	Passes Completed	Pass Yardage	Passes For Touchdowns	Passes Intercepted
Steve McNair	400	250	3,215	24	7
Peyton Manning	566	379	4,267	29	10
Daunte Culpepper	454	295	3,479	25	11

b. Which quarterback has the highest passer rating?

2. A local department store has scratch-off coupons that offer shoppers a discount of 5%, 10%, 15%, and 25% off any item.

a. What are the least and the greatest possible costs, including a 6% sales tax, for a shirt listed at $24.99?

b. Yoshi decides to buy the $24.99 shirt in blue, yellow, and brown. At the checkout counter, he scratches the coupon to find a 15% discount. What does he actually pay, including the 6% sales tax, for the three shirts?

Looking Back and Looking Ahead **77**

Notes _____

_____

_____

_____

c. The store conducted a survey to find out whether the scratch-off coupons had influenced customers to buy. At the end of the day, they tallied the results.

- Would have purchased the items without the coupon: 556
- Were strongly influenced by the coupon: 378
- Were somewhat influenced by the coupon: 137

What percent of customers were influenced in any way by the coupon?

Explain Your Reasoning

When you use mathematical calculations to solve a problem or make a decision, it is important to be able to justify each step in your reasoning.

3. Describe an algorithm for each of the following operations on decimals: addition, subtraction, multiplication, division.

4. Use the algorithms from Question 3 to solve the following problems. Show your steps.

    a. $23.4 + 17.42$ **b.** $43.09 - 17.62$

    c. 3.51×1.2 **d.** $11.7 \div 3$

5. Explain the general procedures you use to answer these questions about percents. Give specific numerical examples.

    a. How do you find the percent equivalent to a given decimal?

    b. How do you find what percent one number is of another?

    c. How do you find a given percent of a number?

Look Ahead

There are many everyday situations and many mathematical contexts that use decimals and percents. You will use the algorithms and concepts developed in this unit in most of the future *Connected Mathematics* units you work on. You will encounter decimals and percents in algebra, geometry, measurement, statistics, and many other areas. Some of the units where you will apply this reasoning include *Filling and Wrapping, Stretching and Shrinking,* and *Data Distributions.*

Notes _____

_____

_____

_____

D

dividend The name for the number into which you are dividing in a division problem. For example, 26.5 is the dividend in the problem 26.5 ÷ 4.

dividendo Nombre del número que divides en un problema de división. Por ejemplo, 26.5 es el dividendo en el problema 26.5 ÷ 4.

divisor The name for the number you are dividing by in a division problem. For example, 4 is the divisor in the problem 26.5 ÷ 4.

divisor Nombre del número por el que divides en un problema de división. Por ejemplo, 4 es el divisor en el problema 26.5 ÷ 4.

P

powers of ten Numbers of the form 10, 10 × 10, 10 × 10 × 10 ... or 10; 100; 1,000; 10,000 ... or 10, 10^2, 10^3 ....

potencias de diez Números en la forma 10, 10 × 10, 10 × 10 × 10 ... ó 10; 100; 1,000; 10,000 ... ó 10, 10^2, 10^3 ....

Q

quotient The name for the answer to a division problem. For example, 6.625 is the quotient to 26.5 ÷ 4.

cociente Nombre del resultado de un problema de división. Por ejemplo, 6.625 es el cociente de 26.5 ÷ 4.

R

repeating decimal A decimal with a pattern of digits that repeats over and over, such as 0.3333333 ... and 0.73737373 .... Repeating decimals are rational numbers.

decimal periódico Un decimal con un patrón de dígitos que se repite una y otra vez, por ejemplo, 0.3333333 ... y 0.73737373 .... Los decimales periódicos son números racionales.

T

terminating decimal A decimal with a representation that ends, or terminates, such as 0.5 or 0.125. Terminating decimals are rational numbers.

decimal finito Un decimal con una representación que termina, como 0.5 ó 0.125. Los decimales finitos son números racionales.

Notes _____

_____

_____

_____

Academic Vocabulary

The following terms are important to your understanding of the mathematics in this unit. Knowing and using these words will help you in thinking, reasoning, representing, communicating your ideas, and making connections across ideas. When these words make sense to you, the investigations and problems will make more sense as well.

D

describe To explain or tell in detail. A written description can contain facts and other information needed to communicate your answer. A diagram or a graph may also be included.
related terms: express, explain, illustrate

Sample: Describe the difference between a terminating decimal and a repeating decimal.

> A repeating decimal repeats a number or a set of numbers over and over again, for example $\frac{1}{3}$ is $0.\overline{3}$. A terminating decimal is a decimal that does not repeat a number or set of numbers, for example $\frac{2}{5}$ is 0.4.

describir Explicar o decir con detalle. Una descripción escrita puede contener hechos y otra información necesaria para comunicar tu respuesta. También se puede incluir un diagrama o una gráfica.
términos relacionados: expresar, explicar, ilustrar

Ejemplo: Describe la diferencia entre un decimal finito y un decimal periódico.

> Un decimal periódico repite un número o un conjunto de números una y otra vez, por ejemplo $\frac{1}{3}$ es $0.\overline{3}$. Un decimal finito es un decimal que no repite un número o conjunto de números, por ejemplo $\frac{2}{5}$ es 0.4.

E

estimate To find an approximate answer that is relatively close to an exact amount.
related terms: approximate, guess

Sample: Jonathan takes $10.00 with him to lunch. He orders a chicken sandwich for $1.99, a side salad for $1.79, a yogurt for $1.29, and a soda for $0.99. Estimate the total cost for Jonathan's lunch and the amount of change he should receive from $10.00.

> I used benchmarks to make my estimate. The sandwich is close to $2.00, the salad $1.75, the yogurt $1.25, and the soda $1.00.
>
>
>
> The total cost of the lunch is about $6.00. Since $10.00 − $6.00 = $4.00, he should receive about $4.00 in change.

estimar Hallar una respuesta aproximada que esté relativamente cerca de una cantidad exacta.
términos relacionados: aproximar, conjeturar

Ejemplo: Jonathan tiene $10.00 para el almuerzo. Ordena un sándwich de pollo por $1.99, una ensalada pequeña por $1.79, un yogurt por $1.29 y un refresco por $0.99. Estima el costo total del almuerzo de Jonathan y el cambio que debería recibir por $10.00.

> Usé puntos de referencia para hacer mi estimado. El sándwich costó cerca a $2.00, la ensalada a $1.75 y el refresco a $1.00.
>
>
>
> El costo total del almuerzo es de alrededor a $6.00. Puesto que $10.00 − $6.00 = $4.00, él debe recibir alrededor de $4.00 de cambio.

Notes _____

_____

_____

_____

explain To give facts and details that make an idea easier to understand. Explaining can involve a written summary supported by a diagram, chart, table, or a combination of these.
related terms: describe, show, justify, tell, present

Sample: Using a 6% sales tax, explain how to find the total cost for a pack of tennis balls priced at $10.00.

> To find the sales tax, change 6% to 0.06. Then multiply the price of the tennis balls by 0.06. $10 × 0.06 = $0.60. Add this to the cost of the tennis balls. $10 + $0.60 = $10.60.

explicar Dar hechos y detalles que hacen que una idea sea más fácil de comprender. Explicar puede implicar un resumen escrito apoyado por hechos, un diagrama, una gráfica, una tabla o una combinación de éstos.
términos relacionados: describir, mostrar, justificar, decir, presentar

Ejemplo: Usando un impuesto sobre ventas de 6%, explica cómo hallar el costo total de un paquete de pelotas de tenis que cuesta $10.00.

> Para hallar el impuesto sobre ventas, cambio 6% a 0.06. Luego multiplica el precio de las pelotas de tenis por 0.06. $10 × 0.06 = $0.60. Suma esto al costo de las pelotas de tenis. $10 + $0.60 = $10.60.

F

find To calculate or determine.
related terms: solve, locate

Sample: Find the value of N. Writing a fact family may help.

$$4.5 \div N = 9$$

> I first wrote down the fact family.
> $4.5 \div N = 9$ $4.5 \div 9 = N$ $9 \times N = 4.5$
> I then found the quotient of $4.5 \div 9$. Since $4.5 \div 9 = 0.5$, $N = 0.5$.

hallar Calcular o determinar.
términos relacionados: resolver, localizar

Ejemplo: Halla el valor de N. Escribir una familia de operaciones puede ayudar.

$$4.5 \div N = 9$$

> Primero escribí la familia de operaciones.
> $4.5 \div N = 9$ $4.5 \div 9 = N$ $9 \times N = 4.5$
> Luego hallé el cociente de $4.5 \div 9$. Puesto que $4.5 \div 9 = 0.5$, $N = 0.5$.

U

use To draw upon given information to help you determine something else.
related terms: utilize, employ

Sample: Consider the following fractions and their decimal representations.

$\frac{1}{9} = 0.1111111...$ $\frac{2}{9} = 0.2222222...$ $\frac{3}{9} = 0.3333333...$

Use the pattern you see to write decimal representations for $\frac{7}{9}$ and $\frac{8}{9}$.

> When the denominator is 9, the digit in the numerator repeats in the decimal representation. Therefore, $\frac{7}{9} = 0.7777777777...$ and $\frac{8}{9} = 0.8888888888....$

usar Recurrir a información dada para ayudarte a determinar algo más.
términos relacionados: utilizar, emplear

Ejemplo: Considera las siguientes fracciones y sus representaciones decimales.

$\frac{1}{9} = 0.1111111...$ $\frac{2}{9} = 0.2222222...$ $\frac{3}{9} = 0.3333333...$

Usa el patrón que ves para escribir las representaciones decimales para $\frac{7}{9}$ y $\frac{8}{9}$.

> Cuando el denomindador es 9, el dígito en el numerador se repite en la representación decimal. Por lo tanto, $\frac{7}{9} = 0.7777777777...$ y $\frac{8}{9} = 0.8888888888....$

Academic Vocabulary   **81**

Notes _____

_____

_____

_____

Index

82 Bits and Pieces III

Notes

_____

_____

_____

_____

Notes _____

_____

_____

_____

Acknowledgments

Team Credits

The people who made up the **Connected Mathematics 2** team—representing editorial, editorial services, design services, and production services—are listed below. Bold type denotes core team members.

Leora Adler, Judith Buice, Kerry Cashman, Patrick Culleton, Sheila DeFazio, Richard Heater, **Barbara Hollingdale, Jayne Holman,** Karen Holtzman, **Etta Jacobs,** Christine Lee, Carolyn Lock, Catherine Maglio, **Dotti Marshall,** Rich McMahon, Eve Melnechuk, Kristin Mingrone, Terri Mitchell, **Marsha Novak,** Irene Rubin, Donna Russo, Robin Samper, Siri Schwartzman, **Nancy Smith,** Emily Soltanoff, **Mark Tricca,** Paula Vergith, Roberta Warshaw, Helen Young

Additional Credits

Diana Bonfilio, Mairead Reddin, Michael Torocsik, nSight,Inc.

Technical Illustration

WestWords, Inc.

Cover Design

tom white.images

Photos

2 t, Michael Newman/PhotoEdit; **2 b,** Susan Findlay/Masterfile; **3,** Lee Foster/Lonely Planet Images; **5,** Ronnie Kaufman/Corbis; **6,** David Young-Wolff/PhotoEdit; **8,** Jeff Greenberg/Omni Photo Communications, Inc.; **11,** Mark Gibson/Index Stock Imagery, Inc.; **14,** Lori Adamski Peek/Getty Images, Inc.; **19,** David Young-Wolff/PhotoEdit; **23,** Tony Freeman/PhotoEdit; **25,** Richard Haynes; **31,** Michael Newman/PhotoEdit; **36,** Warren Lynch/Getty Images, Inc.; **37,** Creatas/PictureQuest; **39,** Richard Haynes; **46,** AP Photo/Mark Humphrey; **50,** Tony Freeman/PhotoEdit; **54,** Dennis MacDonald/AGE Fotostock; **56,** Susan Findlay/Masterfile; **57,** C Squared Studios/PictureQuest; **62,** Dorling Kindersley; **69,** Geoff Dann/Dorling Kindersley; **72 both,** Creatas/Alamy; **76,** Photodisc/Getty Images, Inc.

Data Sources

NFL® and passer rating categories on page 76 are Copyright © NFL Enterprises LLC. Used by permission of the National Football League Properties (NFLP).

NFL®, passer rating formula, and 2003 quarterback statistics on page 77 are Copyright © NFL Enterprises LLC. Used by permission of the National Football League Properties (NFLP).

Note: Every effort has been made to locate the copyright owner of the material reprinted in this book. Omissions brought to our attention will be corrected in subsequent editions.

Notes _____

_____

_____

_____

Labsheet 2.4

Number Sets

Set A
21 × 100
21 × 10
21 × 1
21 × 0.1
21 × 0.01
21 × 0.001

Set B
2.1 × 100
2.1 × 10
2.1 × 1
2.1 × 0.1
2.1 × 0.01
2.1 × 0.001

Set C
0.21 × 100
0.21 × 10
0.21 × 1
0.21 × 0.1
0.21 × 0.01
0.21 × 0.001

Labsheet 4.1

Percent Bars

0%   100%

0%   100%

0%   100%

0%   100%

0%   100%

0%   100%

0%   100%

0%   100%

Labsheet 4.2A

Menu

Larry's Lunch Place

Lunch Specials

Roast Turkey.................................. 3.95
Slices of turkey breast, savory dressing,
homemade gravy, and cranberry sauce

Veggie Quesadilla 3.95
Whole-wheat tortillas stuffed with tomatoes,
roasted peppers, and three kinds of cheese

Chicken Tenders 4.50
Strips of all-white-meat chicken baked
to a golden brown, served with a baked
potato, coleslaw, and barbeque sauce

Larry's Famous Burgers

**Quarter Pound
Hamburger Platter**....................... 3.30

**Quarter Pound
Cheeseburger Platter**.................. 3.60

Larry's Special.............................. 4.35
Two patties, with crisp lettuce, Larry's own
sauce, and cheese on a specially baked bun

Seafood

Shrimp Cocktail 6.95
Tender steamed shrimp served on ice
with tangy cocktail sauce

Fish and Chips 4.45
Three deep-fried fillets with french fries,
coleslaw, and tartar sauce

Baked Meatloaf............................ 3.95
Tasty homestyle meatloaf with mixed
green salad

Spaghetti with Tomato Sauce......3.25
A generous portion of pasta with zesty
sauce, parmesan cheese, and garlic bread

Grilled Chicken Breast.................. 5.25
Served over rice with lemon parsley sauce,
crisp lettuce, tomato slices, and whole
wheat rolls (low cholesterol)

Desserts

Fresh Strawberry Pie.................... 1.89
With frozen yogurt................................2.25
Chocolate Cake 1.50
With ice cream 1.95

Beverages

Coffee, Regular or Decaffeinated .... .80
Hot or Iced Tea..................................... .80
White or Chocolate Milk..................... .99
Lemonade... .99
Soft Drinks.. .99
Orange Juice.. .99
Hot Chocolate...................................... .99
Root Beer Float 1.99

Labsheet 4.2B

Order Check

Larry's Lunch Place Food Order

Item	Price

Date	Server	Table	Guests	Check
				35412

Labsheet 5.3

Circle Graphs

Crime-Lab Technicians

Private Investigators

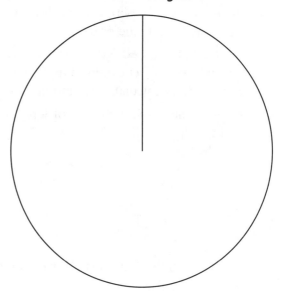

Cats Sleep in the Same Room

Dogs Sleep in the Same Room

Labsheet

Ordering From a Catalog

1. Find three different items you would like to order from a catalog. Each item must cost at least $10.00. On the back of your paper, tape pr glue the picture of the item and its description, or draw a picture of the item and write out its description. Include the price.

2. Complete the attached order form as if you were ordering your three items from the C.M. Project catalog. On the back of the order form, show all the work you did to calculate the amounts for shipping and tax.

3. **a.** Choose one of the items you ordered. List the item with a brief description and give its price.

   b. What would this item cost if it were on sale for 25% off? Show how you found your answer.

   c. What would the item cost if it were on sale for $\frac{1}{3}$ off? Show how you found your answer.

4. Suppose another catalog has your first item listed for $5.00 less than the price you have listed. A third catalog has your item marked down 20%. If shipping charges and tax are the same, which is the better deal for you, and why?

Labsheet

C.M. Project Catalog Order Form

Shipping Address
Name _____
Address _____
City _____ State __ Zip Code _____
Phone (   ) _____

To speed up your order, use our toll-free number 24 hours a day, 7 days a week—100% of the time! 1-800-PER-CENT

Item No.	Description	Size	Color	Qty.	Price/Unit	Total
			Merchandise Total			
			Shipping (10% of Merchandise)			
			Tax (_____)			
			TOTAL			

Method of Payment
☐ Charge to:
_____ VISA   _____ MASTERCARD
Credit Card # _____
Expiration Date ____ / ____ / ____
☐ Check or Money Order
Signature _____

PACING: _____

Mathematical Goals

_____
_____
_____
_____

Launch

_____
_____
_____
_____
_____
_____
_____

Materials

Explore

_____
_____
_____
_____
_____
_____
_____

Materials

Summarize

_____
_____
_____
_____
_____
_____
_____

Materials

Glossary

D

dividend The name for the number into which you are dividing in a division problem. For example, 26.5 is the dividend in the problem 26.5 ÷ 4.

divisor The name for the number you are dividing by in a division problem. For example, 4 is the divisor in the problem 26.5 ÷ 4.

P

powers of 10 Numbers of the form 10, 10 × 10, 10 × 10 × 10. . . or 10; 100; 1,000; 10,000. . . or 10, 10^2, 10^3. . . .

Q

quotient The name for the answer to a division problem. For example, 6.625 is the quotient to 26.5 ÷ 4.

R

repeating decimal A decimal with a pattern of digits that repeats over and over, such as 0.3333333. . . and 0.73737373. . . . Repeating decimals are rational numbers.

T

terminating decimal A decimal with a representation that ends, or terminates, such as 0.5 or 0.125. Terminating decimals are rational numbers.

Index

Acknowledgments

Team Credits

The people who made up the **Connected Mathematics2** team—representing editorial, editorial services, design services, and production services—are listed below. Bold type denotes core team members.

Leora Adler, Judith Buice, Kerry Cashman, Patrick Culleton, Sheila DeFazio, Richard Heater, **Barbara Hollingdale, Jayne Holman,** Karen Holtzman, **Etta Jacobs,** Christine Lee, Carolyn Lock, Catherine Maglio, **Dotti Marshall,** Rich McMahon, Eve Melnechuk, Kristin Mingrone, Terri Mitchell, **Marsha Novak,** Irene Rubin, Donna Russo, Robin Samper, Siri Schwartzman, **Nancy Smith,** Emily Soltanoff, **Mark Tricca,** Paula Vergith, Roberta Warshaw, Helen Young

Additional Credits

Diana Bonfilio, Mairead Reddin, Michael Torocsik, nSight, Inc.

Technical Illustration

Schawk, Inc.

Cover Design

tom white.images